D1594806

Lean ISO 9001

Also available from ASQ Quality Press:

Out of Another @#&*% Crisis!: Motivation through Humiliation
Mike Micklewright

A Practical Field Guide for ISO 9001:2008
Erik Valdemar Myhrberg

ISO 9001:2008 Explained, Third Edition
Charles A. Cianfrani, Joseph J. Tsiakals, and John E. (Jack) West

*Cracking the Case of ISO 9001:2008 for Manufacturing: A Simple Guide to
Implementing Quality Management in Manufacturing,* Second Edition
Charles A. Cianfrani and John E. (Jack) West

*Cracking the Case of ISO 9001:2008 for Service: A Simple Guide to
Implementing Quality Management in Service Organizations,* Second Edition
Charles A. Cianfrani and John E. (Jack) West

*ISO 9001:2008 Internal Audits Made Easy: Tools, Techniques, and Step-by-Step
Guidelines for Successful Internal Audits,* Third Edition
Ann W. Phillips

ISO Lesson Guide 2008: Pocket Guide to ISO 9001-2008, Third Edition
Dennis R. Arter and J.P. Russell

*Making Government Great Again: Mapping the Road to Success with
ISO 9001:2008*
John D. Baranzelli, P.E.

Learning Lean 5S: Quality Pocket of Knowledge (QPoK)
ASQ

Lean Kaizen: A Simplified Approach to Process Improvements
George Alukal and Anthony Manos

*Lean for Service Organizations and Offices: A Holistic Approach for Achieving
Operational Excellence and Improvements*
Debashis Sarkar

5S for Service Organizations and Offices: A Lean Look at Improvements
Debashis Sarkar

*The Executive Guide to Understanding and Implementing Lean Six Sigma: The
Financial Impact*
Robert M. Meisel, Steven J. Babb, Steven F. Marsh, and James P. Schlichting

To request a complimentary catalog of ASQ Quality Press publications,
call 800-248-1946, or visit our Web site at http://www.asq.org/quality-press.

Lean ISO 9001

Adding Spark to Your ISO 9001 QMS and Sustainability to Your Lean Efforts

Mike Micklewright

ASQ Quality Press
Milwaukee, Wisconsin

American Society for Quality, Quality Press, Milwaukee 53203
© 2010 by Mike Micklewright
All rights reserved. Published 2010
Printed in the United States of America
16 15 14 13 12 11   5 4 3 2

Library of Congress Cataloging-in-Publication Data

Micklewright, Mike.
  Lean ISO 9001 : adding spark to your ISO 9001 QMS and sustainability to your
lean efforts / Mike Micklewright.
     p. cm.
  Includes bibliographical references and index.
  ISBN 978-0-87389-784-6 (hardcover : alk. paper)
  1. ISO 9001 Standard 2. Quality control—Standards. 3. Industrial efficiency.
4. Lean manufacturing. I. Title.

  TS156.M512 2010
  658.5—dc22   2010006446

ISBN: 978-0-87389-784-6

Publisher: William A. Tony
Acquisitions Editor: Matt T. Meinholz
Project Editor: Paul O'Mara
Production Administrator: Randall Benson

ASQ Mission: The American Society for Quality advances individual, organizational,
and community excellence worldwide through learning, quality improvement, and
knowledge exchange.

Attention Bookstores, Wholesalers, Schools, and Corporations: ASQ Quality Press
books, video, audio, and software are available at quantity discounts with bulk
purchases for business, educational, or instructional use. For information, please
contact ASQ Quality Press at 800-248-1946, or write to ASQ Quality Press,
P.O. Box 3005, Milwaukee, WI 53201-3005.

To place orders or to request ASQ membership information, call 800-248-1946. Visit our
Web site at http://www.asq.org/quality-press.

 Printed on acid-free paper

Quality Press
600 N. Plankinton Avenue
Milwaukee, Wisconsin 53203
Call toll free 800-248-1946
Fax 414-272-1734
www.asq.org
http://www.asq.org/quality-press
http://standardsgroup.asq.org
E-mail: authors@asq.org

Table of Contents

List of Figures and Tables

A Few Things About the Format of This Book

Perhaps because of the almost sick way I grew up—and many of us grew up—reaching the goal was always the most important thing, even if the process along the way to reaching that goal was usually a laborious chore. This mind-set has been prevalent even when I have read books, and I have read many books. It's hard for me to put a book down and stop reading it, even if it's a bad book. I feel like somehow, something very interesting will eventually come of the book, and I do not want to miss it. Plus, I want the credit, from myself, for completing the book. I can not give myself credit for a book only half completed. Also, I have other books waiting in queue and I want to get to them as quickly as possible, but I'm still reading the boring book and the possible good books will just have to wait.

So, with time I have learned that it is the process of gaining knowledge that is most important and not how many books have been completed. If I begin to read a book in which the knowledge gained is little compared to the time put into reading the book, I will put it down and start with a new book. This has been difficult to do because it goes against what I have come to expect in the form of a grade, gold star, diploma, degree, certificate, merit raise based on performance, and Black Belt.

Oftentimes, I find myself angry about the beginning sections of books. There are always sections like Contents, Acknowledgments, Preface, Foreword, Introduction, and Dedication. I want to tell the authors and publishers that if you want me to read those sections, then give me credit for reading those sections. It's not fair to number those pages with an extinct Roman numeral system. That's crazy. No one uses Roman numerals anymore except when counting Super Bowls. And even then, how many average football fans would know that Super Bowl XXXVIII was really Super Bowl 38? So why do we use Roman numerals at the beginning of books? If someone asks me how long a certain book was that I really enjoyed, I might say, "It was 322 pages, but if you count all the $@#* pages at the beginning that I did not get credit for, it was 351 pages." Now does that not sound so much more impressive than just 322 pages?

So, I feel like protesting, but I don't because my Roman Catholic upbringing makes me feel guilty for claiming that I read a book when in fact I did not read the opening sections with the Roman numerals. What a coincidence—the word Roman was used twice in the above sentence. So I read all the opening sections, with a great deal of reluctance and feeling a little pissy. Sometimes, though, I do not read all of the Acknowledgments and I feel a little better.

So, the good news is that in this book you get credit for reading everything. No Roman numerals! (Now, perhaps the Super Bowl will be encouraged to change its numbering system?!) This should make you feel accomplished already.

Also, because I have grown up to be more goal oriented, I never really care about what page I'm on. I'm only concerned with how many *more* pages I have left to read. So I do calculations in my head to figure out what percent of the book I've completed toward the end goal. (For instance, if I'm on page 140 of a 350-page book, that's about 2/7 complete, which equates to about 28% done. In my mind, the important numbers are that I have 210 pages left to read and I am 28% done.)

Again, it's not the knowledge that counts in my sick world, it's how many books I've read, including the percentage of the book I'm currently reading.

So, the good news in this book is that each page has a page number that represents how many pages are left in the book and the percent of the book completed at that point.

Also, in the example above with the book that contained 350 pages, it officially had 358 pages, but the last eight pages represented the Index. No one reads the Index. I do not even feel the least bit guilty about not reading that section. So, the good news in this book is that the Index will contain the Roman numerals.

ISO 9001

This book refers to ISO 9001 throughout. The reader should be aware that although ISO 9001 is referred to specifically, the same concepts apply to all other quality management system standards that use ISO 9001 as a base, including ISO/TS 16949 (automotive), ISO 13485 (medical devices), TL 9000 (telecommunications), and AS 9100 (aerospace). It also applies to other quality management systems perhaps not based on ISO 9001 (for example, FDA requirements).

SO WHAT IS A PREFACE?

I knew I had to write a Preface, because everyone writes a Preface to their book. I knew that I could not buck the system. I had to work within the system in order to be rewarded by the system—publishers publishing the book. Also, I could not imagine the embarrassment I would suffer if half of the readers who bought my book returned them to Barnes & Noble or Amazon.com with the complaint, "I was ripped off. This book does not have a Preface!"

But I was not sure what a Preface was. I knew the author wrote it, but what does it actually mean, I wondered. "Acknowledgments" is obvious, as is Introduction, Contents, and Dedication.

But what was a Preface? I had always thought a Preface was how someone looked prior to a face-lift and used in a sentence like, "You have such a pretty preface now, you don't need a face-lift." And then when s/he came out of surgery, s/he would have a Postface. Actually, there are two Postfaces. The immediate Postface, which looks like one has been just been mugged, and the longer-term Postface, which looks like one's face wrapped in cellophane.

Oh no, am I going to have to write a Postface also? No one else has, so I will not disturb the system within which I work.

And for that matter, do I need to write a Reverse if I include a Foreword? I won't include a Foreword. That way, I will not need to write a Reverse.

So, Preface is defined on www.answers.com as:

A preliminary statement or essay introducing a book that explains its scope, intention, or background and is usually written by the author.

Here's my Preface . . .

Preface

An engineer working for one of my clients once said, "We can't seem to get our designs completed on time because of ISO."

I told him that the ISO 9001 standard wants their design process to be effective and efficient, and it wants you to meet all of your customer's needs. If your design process is ineffective and inefficient, it is because of how your company designed it; it is not the fault of ISO.

At first blush, one might think "lean ISO" is an oxymoron because of the perception that many people have about an ISO 9001–based quality management system (QMS) that it tends to be slow moving and bureaucratic, with an abundance of useless documents and red tape. But once again, I make the same comment. It's the organization's QMS and your processes that are slow moving, bureaucratic, and rife with an abundance of useless documents and red tape. ISO 9001, or any standard that uses ISO 9001 as its base, wants you to be *effective* and *efficient*. Those words are repeated many times in ISO 9004, the guidance standard for performance improvements, and are the spirit behind ISO 9001. This is further discussed in Chapter 1.

ISO 9001 is nothing more than the compilation of good business practices that have evolved over many years. I challenge the reader to read ISO 9001 and find one requirement that does not make sense to your organization (if applicable). Lean is nothing more than getting rid of the waste in those practices, making them more effective and efficient, with the objective of reducing lead time.

At second blush, one might also think that I might be somewhat hypocritical in using the term "lean ISO" because in my book *Out of Another @#&*% Crisis!* and in my article "Lean Six Sigma: An Oxymoron" I lambasted the term *Lean Six Sigma* because lean and Six Sigma beliefs are in conflict with each other, and the practices of Six Sigma do not support the principles of lean. In Chapter 1, "Lean and ISO: Two Complementary Forces," I will show how the principles of lean and the principles of ISO 9001 *are* in concert with each other, and I will show how the two can and should be complementary to each other and not wasteful.

So what is *lean ISO 9001?*

There are three main aspects to lean ISO 9001 and each aspect has its own chapter dedicated to it.

In Chapter 2, I describe "Leaning Out the Documentation System." In every single company I have visited, without fail, nearly every person I have talked to about their QMS has admitted to having an overly complex and lengthy documentation system that has grown out of control and is extremely un-user-friendly. In this chapter, I will discuss how and why documentation systems get out of control, what's wrong with an overly lengthy documentation system, and how to get it back in control and more user-friendly through the use of the lean tool of 5S.

In Chapter 3, "Integrating Lean Practices with the QMS," I describe how certain lean practices such as value stream mapping, 5S, kaizen, and Training Within Industry (TWI) could and should be integrated within the QMS if the company plans to continue to use lean methodologies in the foreseeable future. In this respect, as a company improves its processes, including its lean and continuous improvement processes, it can then change its own methodologies as recorded in its own documentation system rather than in some training manual not owned by the company itself. I will also demonstrate how other key aspects of lean methodologies easily can and should be integrated into the QMS, including the integration of gemba walks with internal quality auditing, recording preventive actions when witnessing waste, and the integration of lean into management review and quality planning.

In Chapter 4, I discuss "Leaning Out the QMS Processes," including eliminating the wastes involved with operating under multiple continuous improvement processes. This chapter will also discuss the relationship between value stream maps and procedures, and it will provide ideas on how to eliminate some of the wastes involved with typical quality processes like record control, internal auditing, corrective/preventive actions, management review, and document control. In document control, the lean principles behind the quick changeover methodology will be deployed to streamline the document modification/approval system, which is in itself a changeover process.

The book ends with Chapter 5, "Lean ISO 9001 Maturity Assessment Model," in which the importance of developing a lean ISO 9001 maturity assessment model is discussed, and examples of how this can be done are provided.

Included in this book are appendices, which are page numbered so you will get credit for reading them. The first appendix contains lean and quality terms. The remaining appendices are articles that have been previously published in various places that offer further detail and support for the messages contained within the book.

Acknowledgments

First and foremost, I must thank Panera Bread for allowing me to spend so much time in your two stores in Arlington Heights, Illinois. You gave me my office away from the office that allowed me to write my first two books almost simultaneously. Yours is a wise business model that provides free Wi-Fi and an endless cup of coffee to those of us who need the background noise and activity and yet the privacy to do our own work without the kids or the TV providing distraction in our own homes. I always made sure I bought at least one meal, as do the other worker bees hacking away at their laptop computers, within your stores. It is a prudent business decision to encourage us to be in your restaurant because we give the appearance of activity within the restaurant even during those slow hours between 3 p.m. and 5 p.m. A restaurant with people present will always encourage more patrons to enter. Smart move!

From a professional standpoint, I thank the following bosses and mentors at my first "real" job with the Saturn Corporation: Jay Wetzel, VP of engineering, who left an everlasting impression on me while working for him in the summer of '85 as a summer student, Ken Franklin for his idealistic practices and beliefs in what Saturn could be, Greg Glos for his trust in me to proceed independently in so much of my work as a manufacturing engineer, and Phil Ross for his mentoring me in the proper way of doing design of experiments (DOE). DOE would later become my springboard into my new career as an independent quality and lean consultant in 1994.

I also wish to thank my other mentors at my second job with Seaquist Valve in Cary, Illinois, including my direct bosses Rick Epstein and Rich Kaleckas, as well as Pat Dougherty, who once told me, "It's easier to ask for forgiveness than permission."

I wish to thank other professionals who have influenced me to write this book and other books, including Don Dinero, Jim Huntzinger, Dwayne Butcher, Nigel Clements, Dr. Tony Burns, and Mark Graban.

I thank certain clients who have had an effect on my continuing education, including Terry Schadeberg, Jim Brizzolara, John Ballun, and Kevin Meyer.

As an avid reader, I have been inspired by many famous writers, including Thomas Jefferson, Benjamin Franklin, Dr. Edward DeBono, John Stossel, Malcolm Gladwell, Ricardo Semler, Herb Kelleher, Howard Schultz, Paul Orfalea, Bill Waddell, Norm Bodek, Jeffrey Liker, Bill Hybels, and of course, my favorite of all, Dr. W. Edwards Deming.

I wish to thank Dirk Dusharme and Mike Richman of *Quality Digest* magazine for allowing me the freedom to be creative and challenging in my writing and videos. So much of the material for this book was developed as I wrote articles and had them published by *Quality Digest*. Without *Quality Digest,* I would not have known how many people actually liked my writing style and what I have to say, and I may never have had the confidence to go ahead and write a book.

I thank my Dad, who died 10 years ago, for giving me his sense of fairness and making me understand "respect for people" many years before business people even heard of this principle as being one of the core principles of the Toyota Way.

I thank my Mom for her care and warmth. I thank my children Marissa, Erika, Cassandra, Ryan, and Samantha for who they are and who they will be.

And I especially thank my dear wife Donna for all of her support, ingenuity, creativity, drive, and patience with me as I put this book together. She is one of the root causes to the content of this book and she is my rock!

1
Lean and ISO 9001: Two Complementary Forces

Lean is defined as:

A systematic approach to identifying and eliminating waste and non-value-added activities, through continuous improvement, by flowing the product at the pull of the customer, and respecting and involving the employees, in pursuit of perfection.

A quality management system also involves, or *should* involve:

- A systematic approach
- Eliminating waste, leading to more effective and efficient processes
- Continuous improvement
- Meeting customer demands
- Involving the people
- Pursuit of perfection

There is no conflict between lean and an ISO 9001–based quality management system. In fact, the two are, or should be, complementary to each other, if developed with this knowledge and wisdom. This chapter will explain why.

A. THE BOOKENDS OF LEAN: THE ISO 9001 QUALITY MANAGEMENT SYSTEM

There are two very common comments that I hear from many of my clients or audience members. One of the comments comes from my lean-oriented clients and the other comes from my quality-oriented clients—as if they should be different.

The comment from the lean-oriented clients is: "The hardest thing about lean is sustaining our improvements."

The comment from quality-oriented clients who are also ISO 9001 certified is: "We received a nonconformity from our registrar auditor for not doing any preventive actions." Many of these same ISO 9001 companies are also on a lean journey.

What a shame! If only these quality and lean people would talk to each other and not treat each other as separate departments with separate goals. Lean and quality are both about continuous improvement. Let's work together, people!

> *The hardest thing about lean is sustaining our*
> *improvements.*
>
> —Spoken by "lean" personnel

In this section, a number of "lean" terms will be referred to. If the reader is unfamiliar with any of these terms, you may refer to Appendix A, "Lean and Quality Terms" for clarification.

So, the hardest thing about lean is sustaining improvements? Then why not use your ISO 9001–based QMS to control the improvements? ISO 9001 is all about controlling an organization's operations, including those that were just improved through kaizen or a 5S event. When used properly, an ISO 9001–based QMS should help to ensure discipline and adherence to lean practices and improved processes approved by a process owner (quality speak) or a value stream manager (lean speak).

The following lists some of the general requirements of ISO 9001 and how they relate to lean practices.

In section 4.2.1 of ISO 9001, it is stated:

> *The quality management system shall include*
>
> d) *documents, including records, determined by the*
>   *organization to be necessary to ensure the effective*
>   *planning, operation, and control of its processes.*

Those documents might include "lean" documents like standard work combination sheets, kanbans, 5S assessment forms, leader standard work, and/or job breakdown sheets resulting from Training Within Industry's (TWI) Job Instruction training module.

In section 5.4.2 of ISO 9001, it is stated:

Top management shall ensure that

b) the integrity of the quality management system is maintained when changes to the quality management system are planned and implemented

These "changes" might include the improvements made during a value stream mapping or kaizen project, or better yet, the changes that come from *any and all* employees after developing a lean culture that includes the use of leader standard work, daily accountability meetings, visual management, and gemba walks.

In section 5.6.2 of ISO 9001, it is stated:

The input to management review shall include information on

c) process performance and product conformity

d) status of preventive and corrective actions

f) changes that could affect the quality management system

"Process performance" metrics can and should include such typical lean metrics as hourly/daily metrics located on daily production boards, cycle times, throughput, first-pass yield, inventory turns, adherence to kanban quantities, and 5S assessment scores.

Preventive actions should be recorded any time waste is observed, and should be used to initiate kaizen events. After all, wastes such as excessive transportation and/or inventory can lead to problems, and the identification and elimination of these are actions that prevent problems before they happen, thus they are preventive actions. This will be discussed in more depth below and in Chapter 3. The status of these actions and the sustainability of these actions should be reviewed and assessed in management review.

Once again, "changes," as completed during value stream mapping or kaizen events, that could affect the quality management system should be reviewed in management review as another means of helping to sustain improvements.

In section 6.3 of ISO 9001, it is stated:

The organization shall determine, provide and maintain the infrastructure needed to achieve conformity to product requirements. Infrastructure includes, as applicable

a) buildings, workspace, and associated utilities

b) process equipment (both hardware and software)

These requirements will help to sustain any improvements made through the typical use of "lean" tools such as 5S (sort, set in order, shine, standardize, sustain) and TPM (total productive maintenance) efforts.

In section 7.5.1 of ISO 9001, it is stated:

The organization shall plan and carry out production and service provision under controlled conditions. Controlled conditions shall include, as applicable,

> *a) the availability of information that describes the characteristics of the product*

> *b) the availability of work instructions, as necessary*

Kanban cards, used in the lean world, contain information that describes the characteristics of product. Work instructions can include standard work combination sheets, visual instructions, and/or job breakdown sheets, which are generated from the Job Instruction module of Training Within Industry (TWI).

In section 7.5.5 of ISO 9001, it is stated:

The organization shall preserve the product during internal processing and delivery to the intended destination in order to maintain conformity to requirements.

This ISO requirement supports maintaining and sustaining kanban levels and should help ensure that inventory levels are kept to a minimum, helping to preserve the product. This is best done through the use of the lean practices of continuous flow and U-shaped cells.

In section 8.2.2 of ISO 9001, it is stated:

The organization shall conduct internal audits at planned intervals to determine whether the quality management system

> *b) is effectively implemented and maintained*

It further states:

The management responsible for the area being audited shall ensure that any necessary corrections and corrective actions are taken without undue delay to eliminate detected nonconformities and their causes.

All lean efforts are about making a company's processes more effective. The internal audit system, if done correctly, will help to ensure sustainability of improvements made during value stream mapping, kaizen events, and day-to-day improvements made as a result of a developed lean culture.

In section 8.2.3 of ISO 9001, it is stated:

The organization shall apply suitable methods for monitoring and, where applicable, measurement of the quality management system processes. These methods shall demonstrate the ability of the processes to achieve planned results. When planned results are not achieved, correction and corrective action shall be taken, as appropriate.

This requirement supports the need for visual management and lean culture and, again, is another requirement that will support the sustainability of lean improvements, if done properly.

In section 8.5.3 of ISO 9001, it is stated:

The organization shall determine action to eliminate the causes of potential nonconformities in order to prevent their occurrence.

Any time there is overproduction, waiting, not using employees' skills, excessive transportation, inventory, motion, or processing (seven of the *8 process wastes*), observed by anyone, these are causes of potential nonconformities. This requirement should encourage sustainability of lean improvements through the identification of more waste.

More about this in the following section.

> *We received a nonconformity from our registrar auditor for not doing any preventive actions.*
>
> —Spoken by "quality" personnel

If your organization is ISO 9001 certified *and* is on a lean journey, receiving a nonconformity for showing no evidence of completing a preventive action is surely a sign that your quality and lean folks are not talking to each other!

As shown above, seven of the eight generally accepted process wastes should be generating preventive actions, the same actions that should and could result in a kaizen event or action. The only process waste that would not generate a *preventive* action is "defects" because a defect would generate a *corrective* action.

As an example of one of the other seven process wastes initiating a preventive action, a person within an organization witnessed that a skid of product was transported from point A to point B without any value added to the product, and then it was moved again from point B to point C with no value added, and then it was moved again from point C to point D with no value added. This would be considered an example of waste in the form of excessive *transportation*. It is not lean. If the observer of this wasteful action wanted to document what she saw so that action could be taken, she would not write a corrective action because what she saw 1) doesn't *not* conform to ISO 9001 requirements (there is no requirement that states "there shall not be excessive transportation of product") and 2) most probably doesn't *not* conform to an internal requirement of not allowing for excess transportation.

However, because the excessive transportation could result in a nonconformity because the skid of products could *potentially* be scratched, dinged, damaged, contaminated, or lost, a preventive action should be initiated. If auditors were taught how to look for waste in support of a company's lean efforts and ISO 9001 efforts, there would be plenty of preventive actions written. Ideally, an organization would have more preventive actions than corrective actions in a truly well-functioning lean ISO 9001 system.

Why Should a Preventive Action Be Recorded, When We Can Just Initiate a Kaizen Event?

Two reasons:

1. A proper preventive action process and form will force root cause analysis (RCA). RCA should always be done prior to any lean activity and, in reality, it rarely is. Teams or individuals too often haphazardly begin to apply lean tools like 5S, TPM, quick changeover, or value stream mapping without understanding the problem and the root cause(s) of the problem.

2. A proper preventive action process and form will require verification of effectiveness of eliminating the root causes of problems. This is oftentimes overlooked after a kaizen event.

The Bookends

QMS_{LEAN}QMS

In a system in which the quality/ISO people are talking and working with the lean people, or better yet, they are the same people, one would witness (1) that the quality management system would initiate preventive actions, which are in essence kaizen activities, (2) the kaizen activities would occur in the name of lean, and (3) the improvements would be maintained with the help of the quality management system.

In this way, and in so many other ways, lean and ISO 9001 become complementary forces that increase the effectiveness of both!

B. BUT ISO IS SO BORING AND OLD, AND LEAN IS SO EXCITING AND NEW

The president of a transmission remanufacturing facility, which I had previously helped get QS-9000 certified and then ISO/TS 16949 certified, was just beginning to move his organization into the lean world, without my assistance. He asked me one day what I thought of his new Waste Walk form. I asked what the purpose of the form was. He said that it was for anyone to record waste when they saw waste so that a kaizen activity could begin.

I reviewed the form and observed that his Waste Walk form had a Waste Description section, a Root Cause section, a Short-Term Action Plan section, a Long-Term Action Plan section, and a Verification of Results section.

I told the President point blank that his Waste Walk form was *wasteful*. He was taken aback and asked why. I said it was wasteful because it was nearly exactly the same as his Corrective/Preventive Action form in his QMS. Redundancy is wasteful. I also told him that because of this redundancy, it would confuse the employees regarding what form or system to use. He defended his form by stating that ISO was done quite some time ago and he did not want to taint the new lean movement with something so old.

In his mind, his ISO 9001–based quality management system was something they had to do for the customer, something they did not get much for in return, and something that was old and boring.

Also, in his mind, that lean stuff was new and exciting. That was the new wave. That was the future. It has nothing to do with that quality/ISO stuff. Do not mix the two because ISO will dilute what I'm trying to do with lean.

This president had no concept that his first endeavor in building a lean practice was indeed anti-lean.

It's a Bad Parent/Child Relationship

If a company has not seen the benefits of ISO 9001, it is not ISO's fault; it is the company's systems' fault. I dare anyone to identify one requirement within ISO 9001 that does not make good business sense. ISO 9001 is only a compilation of good business requirements that have been developed over many years. ISO 9001 does not conflict with lean principles and in fact supports them as was shown above and will be demonstrated in the next section.

The problem is that most companies have done very little to build upon the basic requirements of ISO 9001 and have learned to "just get by" so that they can earn or maintain their reward—an ISO 9001 certificate. Earning the certificate, and maintaining it, has become the goal, not the improvement of business systems. There are very few companies that have truly lived by the spirit of ISO 9001. If companies did, they would have built their own lean and/or best practices based on the somewhat intentionally vague requirements and principles of ISO 9001, and ISO 9001 would have been just as exciting as lean is now.

But most companies, and top management of companies, took on the role of children who had done something wrong each time an audit was scheduled. Their parents, the registrar auditors, would stop by twice a year and check to see if their children were behaving. The night before the parents came home, the children would hide all the bad stuff (working overtime to prepare for the big audit). When the parents arrived at the house, they saw a lot of bad stuff poking out underneath beds and the kitchen table, but the (bad) parents would just pat the little kids' heads and say "nice job" and hand them a lollipop (certificate) as a reward. The president of the company would then congratulate all the other kids on a job well done (at hiding all of the problems). The children would then learn that hiding problems was a good thing, and the practice would continue on for the subsequent surveillance audits. The children were happy! The parents were also happy, because they saw how happy their children were and how happy *their* parents were by bringing home another check.

ISO 9001 is a good standard (that could still be improved quite a bit, but nonetheless good), and if a company lived by the spirit of the standard, it could invent its own "lean" methodologies to improve and would not have to copy the tools developed by companies like Toyota.

The ISO *registration system* (not the standard) is *not* a good system and in need of serious repair or complete replacement with a new system. It is definitely one reason why an ISO 9001–based QMS within so many companies is not driving improvement and is so boring. But it does not have to be that way!

For more information regarding the need to abolish the ISO registration system before it's too late, refer to my previously published article in Appendix B.

C. THE PRINCIPLES BEHIND ISO 9001 AND LEAN

Principles are fundamentally accepted rules of action or conduct that are generally inarguable depending on one's purpose or goal, such as raising a family, playing a sport, or building a business.

Dr. Stephen Covey, in his landmark book *The 7 Habits of Highly Effective People,* wrote:

> *Principles are guidelines for human conduct that are proven to have enduring, permanent value. They're fundamental. They're essentially unarguable because they are self-evident. One way to quickly grasp the self-evident nature of principles is to simply consider the absurdity of attempting to live an effective life based on their opposites. I doubt that anyone would seriously consider unfairness, deceit, baseness, uselessness, mediocrity, or degeneration to be a solid foundation for lasting happiness and success.*[1]

The processes and controls mandated by ISO 9001 and the tools of lean (such as 5S, TPM, quick changeover) will never be of long-term benefit if the principles of the company are not aligned with the principles of ISO 9001 and lean. An organization must determine its core principles and ensure their alignment with the principles of lean and ISO 9001 if lean or the organization's QMS are to be effective within the organization.

First, the principles are to be established, then the culture should be developed to support the principles, then the internal processes (many of them as dictated by ISO 9001) should be developed to support the principles, and finally the tools (that is, lean) should be taught and practiced in support of the principles.

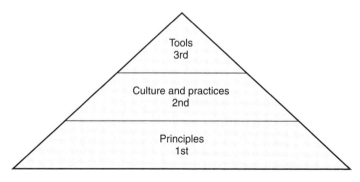

Figure 1.1   Hierarchy of key lean aspects.

Additionally, the principles of lean and ISO 9001 must be aligned and not in conflict with each other.

ISO 9001 is said to be based on the following principles:

1. Customer focus

2. Leadership

3. Involvement of people

4. Process approach

5. System approach to management

6. Continual improvement

7. Factual approach to decision making

8. Mutually beneficial supplier relationships

Given Stephen Covey's definition above, can you imagine running a business on the following "anti-principles," which are the opposite of the above principles?

1. Inward focus to the company

2. Micromanagement

3. Most people not involved in improvement efforts

4. No rhyme or reason to achieving a result

5. Department focus of management

6. Status quo in processes, organization, and culture

7. Decision making based on gut feel (for example, offshoring)

8. Treating suppliers disrespectfully (that is, choosing suppliers based on price tag alone)

Actually, this list of anti-principles is not that far-fetched. It seems that there are more companies aligned with the eight anti-principles than the eight ISO principles. This is not good and this is not the way to run an effective corporation!

Though all of these ISO 9001 principles are sound (and yet vague), the translation of their meaning throughout the ISO 9001 standard varies tremendously. Some of the principles are supported well in the standard (for example, process approach, continual improvement); others are nearly nonexistent throughout the standard (for example, leadership, mutually beneficial supplier relationships). So while the principles of ISO 9001 are not very well supported by the content within the ISO 9001 standard, it is at least important to demonstrate, for the sake of supporting the lean ISO 9001 theme, that the principles of ISO 9001 do indeed support the principles of lean.

Below, the reader will once again observe the list of principles that ISO 9001 is supposed to be based on. Beneath each principle is an explanation of how lean supports that ISO 9001 principle. Also, the sentences in *italics* are the Toyota principles referred to in Jeffrey Liker's excellent book *The Toyota Way*, which defines the 14 principles behind a truly lean organization.

1. *Customer focus.* Lean is about giving the customer what he wants, when he wants it, and in the right quantity. It is very customer oriented.

2. *Leadership.* Lean cultural aspects are very supportive of leadership qualities, including 1) standard work for leaders to ensure accountability and discipline, 2) daily accountability meetings, 3) visual management to ensure assignment of continuous improvement actions, and 4) being at the process. Gemba walks encourage coaching and mentoring, as does the A3 process used in projects and problem solving. Training Within Industry encourages leaders to know and teach the process to those who report to them, as well as how to deal with difficult people situations, and continuous improvement of the process through the three training modules of Job Instruction, Job Relations, and Job Methods, respectively. All of these lean tools and cultural elements strongly support and encourage supervisors to be leaders, not micromanagers.

   > *Principle #1: Base your management decisions on a long-term philosophy, even at the expense of short-term financial goals.*

   > *Principle #9: Grow leaders who thoroughly understand the work, live the philosophy, and teach it to others.*

   > *Principle #12: Go and see for yourself to thoroughly understand the situation.*

3. *Involvement of people.* One of the key pillars of the Toyota Production System and lean has always been "respect for the people." The only way to respect the people is to build a culture that allows the people to improve their own processes rather than having "experts" improve their processes for them.

> *Principle #10: Develop exceptional people and teams who follow your company's philosophy.*
>
> *Principle #13: Make decisions slowly by consensus, thoroughly considering all options; implement rapidly.*

4. *Process approach.* (Note: Those companies who are in the medical device industry and have to comply with the Code of Federal Regulations (CFR) Title 21 for Food and Drugs are still at a disadvantage in understanding the *process approach* due to the fact that the CFR is based on ISO 9001:1994, which was an *element-based* standard, not a process-based standard as are the 2000 and 2008 editions of ISO 9001.)

Value stream mapping, continuous flow, work cells, and reducing inventory in between operations are all key aspects of a lean organization and supportive of a process approach.

Lean encourages leaders to be much more process focused and less short-term-objective focused.

> *Principle #2: Create continuous process flow to bring problems to the surface.*

5. *System approach to management.* Breaking down the barriers between departments for the good of the process is key to a lean organization because the barriers represent waste, and lean is all about getting rid of waste. The system approach to management, though, extends beyond the walls of the organization to the supplier base.

> *Principle #3: Use "pull" systems to avoid overproduction.*
>
> *Principle #4: Level out the workload.*

6. *Continual improvement.* Lean goes beyond *continual* improvement to kaizen, or *continuous* improvement. It's not in conflict with ISO 9001's principle of continual improvement; it just expands the frequency of improvement. Continual improvement implies something that is periodic (that is, an event, a project, or a corrective/preventive action resulting from a customer complaint or internal audit finding). Continuous implies something occurring uninterruptedly in time. True continuous improvement shows itself as little improvements, made every day, by everybody.

Principle #5: Build a culture of stopping to fix problems, to get quality right the first time.

Principle #6: Standardized tasks are the foundation for continuous improvement and employee empowerment. (We will discuss this more in the next section.)

Principle #14: Become a learning organization through relentless reflection and continuous improvement.

7. *Factual approach to decision making.* Daily production charts, visual management, and root cause analysis are all aspects of lean that would support this ISO 9001 principle.

Principle #7: Use only reliable, thoroughly tested technology that serves your people and your processes.

8. *Mutually beneficial supplier relationships.* The value stream extends beyond the walls of one's organization to the suppliers and the entire supply chain. Treating people with respect, a pillar of the Toyota Production System, extends to suppliers as well.

Principle #11: Respect your extended network of partners and suppliers by challenging them and helping them improve.

As one can see, the principles behind ISO 9001 and lean are supportive of each other and in no way are they in conflict with each other.

D. STANDARDIZED TASKS ARE THE FOUNDATION FOR CONTINUOUS IMPROVEMENT AND EMPLOYEE EMPOWERMENT

Chapter 6 of *The Toyota Way,* written by Jeffrey Liker, has the same title as the above heading.

From page 141 of this book:

Ford Motor Company was one of the early mass-production giants associated with rigid standardization on the moving assembly line, and Toyota's approach to standardized work was partially shaped by Henry Ford's view. While Ford eventually became a rigid bureaucracy that followed the destructive practices of Taylor's scientific management, this was not the view that the founder had of standards. Henry Ford's (1988) perspective, written back in 1926, fits well with the Toyota view.

> *Today's standardization . . . is the necessary foundation on which tomorrow's improvement will be based. If you think of "standardization" as the best you know today, but which is to be improved tomorrow—you get somewhere. But if you think of standards as confining, then progress stops.*

Even more influential than Henry Ford was the methodology and philosophy of the American military's Training Within Industry (TWI) service. This program was established in 1940 during WWII to increase production to support the Allied forces. It was based on the belief that the way to learn about industrial engineering methods was through application on the shop floor and that standardized work should be a cooperative effort between the foreman and the worker (Huntzinger 2002).[2]

So much of the Toyota Production System was based on the philosophies of Henry Ford, TWI, and the late great Dr. Deming. Sometimes, it just becomes so apparent how dumbed-down the American management system has become as we now try to copy the Toyota Production System. However, even as we copy Toyota, we still don't get it. We copy the tools of Toyota, not the principles, and therefore will never really change our Western management ways.

From page 143 of *The Toyota Way*:

> *Any good quality manager at any company knows that you cannot guarantee quality with standard procedures for ensuring consistency in the process. Many quality departments make a good living turning out volumes of such procedures. Unfortunately, the role of the quality department is often to assign blame for failing to "follow the procedures" when there is a quality problem. The Toyota Way is to enable those doing the work to design and build in quality by writing the standardized task procedures themselves. Any quality procedures have to be simple and practical enough to be used every day by the people doing the work.[3]*

So procedures and work instructions are an important part of both ISO 9001 *and* lean. It's how they are developed and used that is important. Dr. Deming told us we must "drive out fear!" and yet Jeffrey Liker states above that we often assign blame to people not following the procedures. We are still not following what the late great Dr. Deming taught us. It is the act of using the document as a weapon that gives ISO 9001 a bad name, not the document itself. Until the use of fear is eliminated and the principle of respecting people is adopted, work instructions and procedures will never be effective, nor will any form of standardized work be effective, no matter what format it is in.

Regarding the format that Toyota uses (again, not that it would matter without respecting the people first), Toyota president Fujio Cho states on p. 142 of *The Toyota Way*:

> *Our standardized work consists of three elements—takt time (time to complete one job at the pace of customer demand), the sequence of doing things or sequence of processes, and how much inventory or stock on hand the individual worker needs to have in order to accomplish that standardized work. Based upon these three elements, takt time, sequence, and standardized stock on hand, the standard work is set.*[4]

A work instruction should have the "sequence" covered but not necessarily the takt time or inventory on hand . . . but there's no reason it can't. The important thing is that a company *should not have both* standardized work *and* work instructions. They should be integrated.

Both work instructions and standardized work are built upon and based upon the same premise: it is impossible to improve any process until it is first standardized. One must standardize the process, and thus stabilize it, before continuous improvement can be made.

And this is yet another way in which ISO 9001 and lean complement each other!

E. ISO 9004 AND LEAN

At the time of the writing of this book in the summer of 2009, ISO 9004:2009 was still a work in process, with the anticipated release date being sometime around the very end of 2009 and U.S. publication in early 2010. The anticipated title of the standard will change from the 2000 version, "Quality management systems—Guidelines for performance improvements" to "Managing for the sustained success of an organization—A quality management approach."

Since, as of this writing, ISO 9004:2009 has not been released, this section of the book will address the relationship between ISO 9004:2000 and lean.

ISO 9004 is a guidance document. No company has to comply with it or follow it for any reason. It exists for a company's arbitrary and optional use. ISO 9004, in my opinion, represents the spirit behind ISO 9001. It is what a company would use if it was really trying to use ISO 9001 to improve its operations rather than to just gain a certificate that opens the door to potential new business. It represents the vast possibilities of how a quality management system could be developed to truly improve an organization's operations and systems. It is a good document!

To be honest though, I do not quite understand the tremendous amount of effort and time that has been put forth to update, modify, and improve ISO 9004 when it gets so little use. I teach and give presentations all over North America, and I have yet to find one organization that has used ISO 9004:2000 to improve its quality management systems. Most executives, including many management representatives, have never even heard of the existence of ISO 9004.

The International Organization for Standardization's (ISO) Technical Committee 176 on Quality Management and Quality Assurance is the committee responsible for developing the ISO 9000 series of standards and guidance documents. It is they, and the technical advisory groups within each country, who have spent so much time and put so much effort into radically changing the ISO 9004 standard. But why, I wonder, if there is no incentive to use it or efforts put forth to market its value? It would be like my putting a tremendous amount of effort into writing a second edition to this book, even though I had very few sales of this edition. Why couldn't they put more effort into improving ISO 9001:2008, especially with regard to supporting the eight quality management principles upon which it is supposed to be based?

At an international conference on ISO 9001, lean, and Six Sigma in 2006, a top executive of ANAB (ANSI–ASQ National Accreditation Board) briefed the audience on the upcoming changes to ISO 9001 and ISO 9004. He mainly spoke of the larger, more involved changes to ISO 9004 and stated that ISO 9001 will not change much. He spoke of the many hours that were being devoted to improving ISO 9004. During the Q&A session, I personally asked if ANAB, or some other body, had tried to determine the root cause as to why so many people do not use or are unaware of ISO 9004 before putting so much time and effort into improving it. His response was that there were four or five root causes that were discussed, but there was no agreement as to which ones were the true root causes. He further stated that if "ISO 9004 doesn't work this time, it might just go away. This is the last chance." Isn't this a little like spending a great deal of time and effort on improving fax technology? How can standards professionals spend a great deal of time and money on improving a product without understanding the root cause as to why very few people use the product? Determining root cause is probably the most important part of improving a quality system, and ANAB itself—the organization that accredits the companies that certify your company—does not seem to understand root cause analysis.

Regardless of this issue, the present ISO 9004 standard is a good document, and it does demonstrate a great deal of overlap with and consistency with lean.

Effectiveness and Efficiency

I've known for quite some time that the words "effectiveness and efficiency" were used in tandem a great deal in ISO 9004:2000. So, for the sake of this book, I took it upon myself to actually count the number of times that some form of "effectiveness and efficiency" is used together in tandem. It astounded even me. I counted 86 occurrences! 86!! If anyone was to ever think that the idea of eliminating waste and making processes more efficient was not an important part of ISO 9001, as reflected in its spiritual counterpart, ISO 9004, this fact should dispel that notion.

The term is used throughout the standard and is very prominent in two particular sections:

7.1   Planning of product realization (planning for little waste)

8.2.1.3   Internal audit (looking for waste)

This is the breakdown, by section of ISO 9001/9004, of the number of times some form of the words "effectiveness and efficiency" is used in tandem:

Section #	# of occurrences
4 Quality management system	6
5 Management responsibility	16
6 Resource management	10
7 Product realization	24
8 Measurement, analysis and improvement	30

It is used throughout the standard, and there is a high concentration of it used, predictably, in section 8 "Measurement, analysis and improvement."

An Example of the Use of "Effectiveness and Efficiency": 8.2.1.3 Internal audit (ISO 9004:2000)

In Chapter 3, I make the argument that internal auditors should be looking for waste as they audit, and that when waste is observed they should write up preventive actions.

In support of this argument, Section 8.2.1.3 of ISO 9004 states:

Top management should ensure the establishment of an effective and efficient internal audit process to assess the strengths and weaknesses of the quality management system . . .

The internal audit process provides an independent tool for use in obtaining objective evidence that the existing requirements have been met, since the internal audit evaluates the effectiveness and efficiency of the organization.

Examples of subjects of consideration by internal auditing include

- *Effective and efficient* implementation of processes . . .

- *Effective and efficient* use of statistical techniques . . .

- *Effective and efficient* use of resources . . .

Internal auditors should be looking for waste, in the form of inefficient processes leading to ineffectiveness, and not just compliance. Internal auditors should be supporting the company's lean journey.

Why Are the Terms "Effectiveness" and "Efficiency" Joined Together 86 Times?

Section 8.5.4 of ISO 9004:2000 somewhat defines the two terms as:

- Effectiveness (such as outputs meeting requirements)

- Efficiency (such as resources per unit in terms of time and money)

Furthermore, many people associate the words as such:

- Effectiveness = Quality (or ISO 9001) related

- Efficiency = Lean related

I make the assertion throughout this book that ISO 9001 and lean should be integrated and should be one and the same, just as ISO 9004 asserts that effectiveness and efficiency should be used in tandem. But why?

It's simple. If there is waste in an organization's processes, this will directly negatively affect the resources per unit, in terms of time and money (efficiency), for that organization. As an example, if there's more inventory (one of the 8 process wastes), it costs more to store it, it affects cash flow negatively, and it takes more time to allocate and move the inventory, thus negatively affecting efficiency. If there is excess transportation of product (another one of the 8 process wastes), the organization needs to pay for the extra wages and equipment to move the product, thus negatively affecting the efficiency.

In both cases, quality and on-time delivery may suffer. With regard to inventory, excess inventory can lead to obsolescence, damaged product, contaminated product, lost product, and product that exists beyond the point of expiration or usefulness. Oftentimes when an organization makes extra inventory of one item based on a forecast, it is using capacity that could be used in getting hot products out the door to meet customer demand, which can result in not meeting the customer's delivery requirements. In other words, because of the inventory problem, quality and on-time deliveries do not meet requirements, which is the definition of *not* being effective.

The same can be said of the excess transportation problem. Excess transportation leads to the increased possibility of dropping the product, dinging the product, contaminating the product, and/or losing the product. The company's quality goals may not be met, which is a sign of an ineffective process. Furthermore, because of all of the extra movement, lead time increases and on-time delivery may not be met, which, again, is a sign of an ineffective process.

Just as effectiveness and efficiency should not be separated, neither should quality and lean.

Annex B of ISO 9004

Annex B of ISO 9004:2000 is entitled "Process for continual improvement." The reader is encouraged to read this section of the standard. It starts off with:

> *A strategic objective of an organization should be the continual improvement of processes in order to enhance the organization's performance and benefit its interested parties.*
>
> *There are two fundamental ways to conduct continual process improvement, as follows:*
>
> *a) breakthrough projects which either lead to revision and improvement of existing processes or the implementation of new processes; these are usually carried out by cross-functional teams outside routine operations;*
>
> *b) small-step ongoing improvement activities conducted within existing processes by people.*

Method A in "lean speak" is called *kaizen events* or *kaizen blitzes*.

Method B in "lean speak" is called *developing a lean culture* including the use of leader standard work, daily accountability meetings, visual management, and leadership discipline.

If we were really smart as American businesspeople, we could have developed our own lean methodologies by understanding the spirit behind ISO 9001/9004 and developing our own ways. But then, it's easier to copy other companies like Toyota rather than think for ourselves. (This is called sarcasm.)

F. HOW ISO 9001 AND LEAN MAKE UP FOR EACH OTHER'S WEAKNESSES

ISO 9001 Weaknesses

1. *ISO 9001 only requires* continual *improvement.* These are periodic improvements driven by a customer complaint or an internal audit finding. There's always a good chance that no improvements will be made within an organization for entire days if it abides by only a *continual* improvement process.

Lean is about *continuous improvement,* or *kaizen.* Lean culture elements, such as leader standard work, daily accountability meetings, visual management, and leadership discipline, as defined in David Mann's book *Creating a Lean Culture,* drive improvements made every day, by everybody. As described above, Annex B does encourage *continuous* improvement activities. It just doesn't call it continuous improvement.

Lean encourages "respect for the people." Respect for people includes allowing *all* people to make improvements in *their* area of responsibility, not specialized people from different departments, like those who might wear special Belts, whether they are Black, Green, or Yellow.

2. *ISO 9001 does not define how to improve, it just says do it.* This is not necessarily a bad thing. We should be smart enough to develop our own ways, our own style, our own methodologies. But we don't. So, in typical American fashion, we copy the tools of Toyota. If we only knew how to do root cause analysis well, we could have developed our own 5S, TPM, value stream mapping, or quick changeover processes. No one taught Toyota these tools. They developed the tools on their own as they stuck to their principle of getting to the root causes of problems.

Lean does give us the tools to, as ISO 9001 states, "continually improve the effectiveness of the quality management system," if we so choose to use them. We could choose to use these proven tools, integrate them into our quality management system, and improve upon them.

3. *ISO 9001 does not force us to look for and reduce waste . . . specifically.* ISO 9001 does state repeatedly that we must "continually improve the effectiveness of the quality management system." This means that we should be looking for and eliminating waste. Some might say that reducing waste is improving efficiency, not effectiveness. One might further argue that improving the effectiveness of a QMS is the same as increasing the possibility of attaining a desired outcome (for example, fewer rejects or customer complaints, on-time delivery) and that improving its efficiency is more synonymous with doing more with less resources through waste identification and reduction. But I would contend that keeping effectiveness separate from efficiency is like keeping quality separate from lean. Most people associate "effectiveness" with "quality" and "efficiency" with "lean" (even though one of the 8 process wastes is "defects," a term usually associated with quality, or lack thereof). I teach my students that one example of auditing for *effectiveness* is looking for and identifying waste. This is why: if there is excess inventory, it will lead to defects either in quality, profits, or on-time delivery (building too much of the wrong stuff and being late in delivering the right stuff). It leads to not attaining a desired outcome— the definition of effectiveness. If there is excess transportation within the facility, it can lead to quality problems and on-time delivery problems— again not attaining a desired outcome—or a lack of effectiveness.

In what I refer to as the spirit behind ISO 9001, ISO *9004*:2000 (Quality management systems—Guidelines for performance improvements) also encourages us to audit for both effectiveness and efficiency. Effectiveness and efficiency are intimately related. This is why Dr. Deming stated that the way to increase productivity (efficiency) is by improving quality (effectiveness).

Furthermore, in section 7.5.1 of ISO 9004:2000, it is stated:

> *Top management should go beyond control of the realization processes in order to achieve both compliance with requirements and provide benefits to interested parties. This may be achieved through improving the effectiveness and efficiency of the realization processes and associated support processes, such as*

- *reducing waste*

If we were living by the spirit of ISO 9001, we would have known that reduction of waste is important to any quality management system without having to wait for someone from Toyota to teach us.

Since the *ISO 9001* standard does not specifically use the words "efficiency"—as ISO 9004:2000 does repeatedly—or "reducing waste," and since many people only associate efficiency, and not effectiveness, with waste reduction, many people do not see ISO 9001 as encouraging waste reduction and the lean movement. What a shame! More importantly, what a waste!

4. *ISO 9001 does not necessarily encourage employee involvement.* Even though the third principle behind the ISO 9001 standard is "involvement of people," there really is no requirement within ISO 9001 that compels or encourages employee involvement. ISO 9001 requires communicating to the employees how effective the quality management system is, it requires quality objectives to be relevant at each level within the organization, and it requires the organization to ensure that the employees are competent to do their jobs, but it does not require all employees to be involved.

Lean does encourage all employees to be involved.

Lean Weaknesses

1. *There are few provisions in lean to help sustain improvements.*
   A quality management system is all about controlling operations.
   Section 4.2.1 of ISO 9001 states that an organization must have
   "documents, including records, determined by the organization
   to be necessary to ensure the effective planning, operation
   and control of its processes." Furthermore, control systems
   such as internal audits, management reviews, and verification
   of effectiveness of actions taken are required within an ISO
   9001–based QMS. These requirements should all help sustain
   improvements made.

2. *Training in lean tools is oftentimes initiated randomly, without
   a plan.* Internal audits can point out weaknesses and wastes and
   should be used as an initiating point for kaizen events or training
   in a specific lean tool. When done properly, corrective and
   preventive actions, quality planning, and management reviews
   should also be used to initiate kaizen events and/or training in a
   specific lean tool.

3. *Lean does not require document and record control.* Even though
   there are document requirements in lean, like standard work
   combination sheets, job breakdown sheets, leader standard work,
   and kanbans, there are no requirements for controlling them.

Of course, ISO 9001 requires both documents and records to be controlled.

4. *Lean does not require root cause analysis to be performed prior to implementing actions.* Most lean books do suggest doing root cause analysis, yet, in practice, very few companies really do root cause analysis prior to taking any lean actions or during kaizen events.

ISO 9001 requires RCA to be done. If all waste were properly identified on a corrective and preventive action form, then root cause analysis would be properly done rather than haphazardly selecting a lean tool to use. The root cause of the problem would point to what lean tool should be used, if any at all. The root cause should also determine what training is required for that particular problem at that time, not at some random time as is done within many organizations.

G. IF THEY ARE SO COMPLEMENTARY, WHY ARE THEY NOT INTEGRATED?

Simple! As stated earlier in this chapter, ISO 9001 is old and boring and lean is exciting and new.

Also, ISO 9001 is a *quality* management system run by the *quality* department. The QMS requires a *quality* manual, a *quality* policy, *quality* objectives, *quality* planning, and *quality* records. Most employees think these documents have nothing to do with them unless they are in the quality department. As a result, the quality department is the only department really active within the quality management system.

On the other hand, lean is run by production or operations people. It really has nothing to do with quality, so they oftentimes think, even though one of the 8 wastes is *defects*. Many of these same people still do not buy into what Dr. Deming tried to teach us years ago: if a company improves quality, it will increase production, reduce costs, and increase profits. This relationship is clearly not understood by many people.

As a result, in many American companies we have two opposing camps—ISO 9001 and lean—replacing the two opposing camps of yesteryear—quality and production, respectively—in name only. The opposing camps fight for attention and resources. They do whatever is necessary to achieve their own departmental goals, even if they hurt the overall system.

Top management needs to see the strong relationship between quality and lean and develop the organization so that they are properly integrated and not opposed to each other. Top management needs to understand and properly communicate to the organization that improving quality (through variation reduction) will lead to productivity increases and a leaner environment!

2
Leaning Out the Documentation System

A. ENTROPY

There are some things that you learn about in high school or college that for some strange reason, you never forget. It might be a historical (or Saturday night) date, a fact, a theory, or a formula. You remember it your whole life, even though it may have nothing to do with your life or your profession. For me, it is the word *entropy*. I can remember the meaning clearly without ever having to look it up: *everything proceeds in the direction of disorder*:

If I tell my kids to clean up their room, I witness entropy the next day.

If I clean out my garage, I witness entropy the next week.

If the company cleans out its files, folders, and network, we witness entropy the next month.

If we have the makings of an addiction (such as smoking, drinking, gambling, eating, playing video games), over time entropy sets in.

If we only do the beginning of 5S (sort, straighten, and shine), we witness entropy set in. Our gains are not sustained.

And if we build an ISO 9001–based quality management system with adequate documentation at the beginning, over time we witness entropy set in as the documentation system proceeds in the direction of disorder by growing larger and larger and larger, until such time that it becomes un-user-friendly and cumbersome.

A company's documentation system will continue to grow larger, and entropy will continue to unleash its magical powers, until such time that someone finally puts a control system in place. This is exactly why the fifth S of 5S is *sustain*. "Sustain" exists to fight entropy.

The question I must ask the reader is: what do you have in place to fight entropy in your QMS documentation system? Probably nothing!

Entropy is the big-picture reason why your documentation system is so messed up. Before we start talking about control systems, we must first find out why documentation systems get *fat*—the word I choose to use as the opposite of lean—in the first place.

B. WHY DO DOCUMENTATION SYSTEMS GET FAT?

It is wise for a company to perform its own root cause analysis to discover why its own documentation system is so fat so that a specific corrective action for its own root causes can be developed. In the meantime, here are a few possible reasons as to why a documentation system might get fat:

1. Processes, in the form of documented written procedures or work instructions, are generally developed over many years and oftentimes contain steps that are no longer required because of technology changes. A procedure might still state that an employee must print out a copy and file it away in some filing cabinet even though the same document is saved in an electronic folder. Years ago, before computers, employees had to file copies in hard copy form. No one ever questions whether this is still needed. I have found this particular example rampant in many companies, especially while performing value stream mapping in the office environment.

2. Some processes contain an accumulation of band-aids that were put in place over many years because so many companies do not do a good job of eliminating the root causes of problems. In fact, this is why lean is so popular today—because we have so much waste resulting from employees *not* getting to the root cause of a problem, as demonstrated in these examples:

   - A company sends defective product to a customer. The corrective action is to add inspectors on the production floor and add a checking process after order entry in the office.

- The same company sends critical parts to a customer several days late. The sales manager promises that it will never happen again—*because it will affect his commissions*—and mandates that finished goods inventory needs to be doubled.

The company never determined why the product was defective or why the product was shipped late. However, the problem "went away" and waste was added, the same waste we now try to eliminate in the form of lean activities.

3. Because there are so many possible authors of procedures and work instructions within a company, the same topic is covered in multiple documents without one author realizing that another author covered the same topic in a different document.

4. Some authors believe that recording the same requirement in multiple documents is a good thing, and so they intentionally do so. That way, the readers, they believe, will not miss the requirement. What they fail to understand is that if the process is improved, multiple documents now have to be updated.

5. The same requirement is covered in multiple documents inadvertently. Redundancy is one of the biggest culprits in a fat documentation system. Examples include:

    - The same specification might be recorded on a drawing, a control plan, a check sheet, an inspection sheet, a work order, and a traveler. As I was teaching a group of internal auditors, we traced one specification (representing thousands of others) that was recorded on six different documents. I told the auditors to look for this type of redundancy when they audited because they would most undoubtedly find inconsistencies with the specification between the multiple documents. Sure enough, we did.

    - The same written requirement might be recorded in many different formats. Some people prefer written text over flowcharts or vice versa, so they have both. Oftentimes, procedures, instructions, databases, and forms cover the exact same topic.

6. Many documents are not written in process flow fashion, rather they are written in batches of topics (that is, responsibilities, references). When documents are not written in process flow fashion, they tend to be redundant and overly lengthy.

7. Some authors do not write what the employees actually do. They copy the requirements of the standard and write their documents just like the standard is written. These become useless documents because no one understands them, and yet they are part of the QMS.

8. Some documents do not clearly define responsibility. If they do not, multiple documents tend to state the same actions repeatedly without clearly identifying responsibility.

9. It is stated throughout ISO 9001 that companies are supposed to "continually improve the effectiveness of the quality management system." To many people, this means: add to the documentation system in the form of new sentences, new paragraphs, new work instructions, new procedures, new forms, new instructions on how to fill out a form, new flowcharts, and so on. Many people also feel that to respond to a corrective action properly, there has to be an addition to the corrective action document or even an additional document.

   > *It's ironic how quality/ISO folks are adding to the system while lean folks are trying to simplify the system. This is yet another example of quality and lean folks not working together.*

10. Procedure formats, either purchased or internally developed, encourage non-value-added and redundant sections that are not read or used by the employees, not reviewed by the approvers, and/or are not referred to by the trainers. We will discuss more on this later in the chapter.

11. Similar to the junk we save at home, we don't throw out the documents we never use or have not used for quite some time— just in case we might need them or just in case the auditor might want to see them.

12. Some companies still have leftover procedures from ISO 9001:1994, which has been obsolete since 2003. Back then, many people thought they had to have a separate procedure for every single element number of the 20 elements. This was actually not true. An organization did have to have procedures covering each of the elements, for the most part, but they did not have to be *separate* procedures. A lot of redundancy resulted from this (for example, the same steps being recorded in both the Inspection and Testing procedure and the Inspection and Test Status procedure).

This also discouraged process flow, which added to the waste and redundancy. Many companies still have separate procedures entitled Control of Customer-Supplied Product, Quality System, and/or Statistical Techniques. Oftentimes, these procedures are redundant, meaningless, and/or not applicable. I challenge the reader, if your company was certified prior to the year 2000, to review your system and look for documents like these in your system and determine whether there really is any value in these documents.

13. Some people fear the external auditor and do not want to rock the boat and get rid of any documents that the auditor might notice missing and then issue a nonconformity.

   Many people build their quality management system for their external auditors rather than for the good of their own company.

14. Some external auditors encourage fat documentation systems. A registrar auditor recently asked one of my clients to develop an executive summary of the management review meeting minutes from their already documented meeting minutes so *his* job would be easier to do when he returns every six months for a surveillance audit. Furthermore, he e-mailed the following opportunity for improvement (OFI) to my client after the audit OFI:

   Please add this OFI to your most recent audit report. Call me or e-mail me if you have questions.
   (OFI-1) Readiness for ISO upgrade will require evidence of training to ISO 9001:2008, evidence of a gap analysis, an internal audit to the significant gap analysis items, at least one management review to the auspices of ISO 9001:2008, internal auditors trained to the gap analysis items, a stronger process audit (use of the figure eight concept), organizational embracing of the eight operating principles of ISO 9004:2000, use of the ISO 9001 overview model at management review, and training records that demonstrate that all employees top to bottom have been trained to ISO 9001:2008. The following elements for ISO 9001:2008 have been elevated and will require special attention: (4.1) outsourcing control needs to be defined and (4.2) external documents you'll need to demonstrate good control; be aware that early communications with customers during contract review is subject to audit.

The figure eight method is two butted up circles on a horizontal plane that look like the number 8 on its side. The left-hand circle (part 1) requires the auditor to assess the ISO 9001 standard requirements against your QMS standard for the process and elements that they are required to audit. They should identify any poor correlation, and part 1 must be done before moving to part 2 of the figure eight. There the auditor derives the checklist for observations made by performing part 1 in preparation for assessing conformance of the process to be audited. The auditee is then questioned as normal. The reason for this is that many times the auditor immediately jumps to part 2 without ever reviewing how well the company's QMS matches the requirements of the standard; you'll need to guard against this.

In addition to the executive summary and the figure eight, he also suggested that they develop a separate action sheet, a contingency/ disaster recovery plan, an hourglass model for business planning, and turtle diagrams. The auditor, a former 30-year employee of General Motors, was encouraging a fatter quality management system. Besides the myriad of other problems with his e-mail and his "audit" time, like offering three hours of advice while "auditing," he was helping a little company create a bureaucracy. Additionally, this company of about 20 employees has also received many more documentation suggestions from its one very large client.

There are many other examples of external auditors encouraging the use of potentially non-value-added documents. The use of turtle diagrams is one such example. I have seen many other companies include turtle diagrams in their documentation systems. Without fail, the responsible people all say that the reason they have them is because it was strongly suggested to add them into their QMS by their registrar auditor. I would ask the people if they use them in any way and whether they add value. Without exception, all said that they were of no value in their system. For more information about what I think of turtle diagrams, please read the article I wrote, reprinted as Appendix C, entitled "Turtle Diagrams, Registrar Auditors, and More Waste."

15. Some authors are overly detailed, philosophical, informative, think they know it all, and/or use ISO as a scapegoat to get what they want to have done rather than what adds value.

16. Many authors and management representatives overinterpret the standard's documentation requirements. This occurs frequently!

17. There is no control system to fight entropy. There is nothing in place, nor has there ever been anything in place, to stop the documentation system from growing out of hand.

18. There is no clearly understood differentiation between a procedure and a work instruction, leading to more redundancy.

C. THE DANGERS OF A FAT QMS

At the risk of stating the obvious, a fat documentation system does not work well. An overly lengthy documentation system becomes complex and redundant. It's hard to find specific requirements that one is searching for, it becomes tedious and confusing to the user, so they stop trying to find what they need and they rely on their memory instead.

Like steak that contains too much fat, the fat must be trimmed in order to find the real meat of the situation. A fat documentation system is anti-lean.

Additionally, because the documents are so long and/or there are so many documents, oftentimes the approvers, especially if there are multiple approvers, do not review the documents thoroughly prior to approving them, which increases the chances that the documents and the methodologies are not accurate.

D. ORIGIN OF LEANING OUT THE QMS DOCUMENTATION

Prior to the publication of ISO 9001:2000, I helped companies develop a QMS and get certified to ISO 9001 or ISO 9002 for the first time. These companies had no previous QMS, so I helped them develop a QMS from scratch. After the publication of ISO 9001:2000, some of my work changed to helping companies to *modify* their QMS to one that would meet the requirements of the significantly changed quality management system standard. I worked with QMSs that I did not originally help to establish. These were systems that were either established internally or with the assistance of a different consultant. It was at this time that I realized the waste in so many documentation systems—mostly in the form of redundancy.

The first company I worked with was a small company in Indiana that warehoused steel coils. They had been certified to ISO 9002:1994 and requested my assistance to help them convert to the new standard. Of course, they had 20 procedures (consisting of 80 pages), one for each element of the standard. I showed the client the waste and the redundancy in their procedures, and we set out to reduce their documentation system by writing procedures around what they *actually did*. Then we went back to the standard to ensure compliance. The main difference was that the new QMS was built around their processes first rather than what the standard required first. The end result was a reduction of procedures to 10, consisting of 25 pages. This was a reduction of 50% of the procedures and 69% of the pages.

Soon after, I helped a transmission assembly company in Georgia reduce the number of procedures they had in place from 58 to 28, and then I assisted its sister company in Illinois in reducing the number of documents (procedures, work instructions, and forms) they had from 1100 to 250, and they still had more to eliminate.

Another company that I worked with electronically (I never visited their facility) asked me for recommendations on how to reduce their high number of documents. They had a 75-page quality manual, 27 pages of turtle diagrams, and a 22-page Six Sigma manual. I showed them how to reduce this all down to a five-page manual.

An electronic manufacturing services (EMS) company with headquarters based in Illinois had one corporate quality manual and four other quality manuals (30 pages each on average) representing different standards each of their 14 sites were certified to, as detailed in a separate document called a Registration Matrix. I showed the company how all five manuals and the matrix could be combined into one six-page quality manual. This company also had corporate standard operating procedures that overlapped in large part with site instructions (which were really procedures) and the quality manuals. The sites also had work instructions. I strongly suggested that they eliminate the corporate SOPs and redefine what an SOP is and what a site instruction is. The system was an absolute mess that had been developed over many years with many people involved. The system was very confusing, and it was very difficult to find anything that was needed. When a document could not be found, a new one was generated and the problem perpetuated itself.

With this success and the realization that more and more companies experienced the same problem of massive documentation, I put together a one-hour presentation, which then turned into a half-day workshop, and then, finally, a full-day workshop. Organizations would then hire me to assess their documentation system, make recommendations for leaning out their QMS documentation, modify some of their documentation as an example, and then train their employees on how to lean out their own documentation system. It truly has amazed me, as this topic has grown in popularity, how many companies share the same problem of massive amounts of documentation.

There are two very important facts to point out that are consistent with all of these examples:

1. Important content was *not* eliminated. The documents were *not* made to be more vague. We simply got rid of the junk and the redundancies that did not belong.

2. We did not use a special process to eliminate the junk and the redundancies. We simply used the principle of eliminating waste. A document, or a section of a document, that is not read by any employee, for whatever reason, is wasteful. This was the simple premise. However, for ease of application for the reader, I will show you how the process of 5S could be used to accomplish the same feat of leaning out a company's QMS documentation.

E. USING 5S TO LEAN OUT YOUR QUALITY MANAGEMENT SYSTEM

5S, one of the many lean tools used to drive out waste, originated out of the Toyota Production System and consists of the following Japanese words: *seiri, seiton, seiso, seiketsu,* and *shitsuke.* The English translation of the five S's and a brief definition of each follows:

Sort. Remove all unnecessary materials and equipment.

Set in order (or Straighten). Make it obvious where things belong and that they're easy to get to.

Shine. Clean and inspect everything, inside and out.

Standardize. Establish policies and procedures to ensure that 5S is used throughout the facility consistently.

Sustain. Training, after 5S photos, assessments, and daily 5S activities are completed, to ensure ongoing compliance.

The benefits of 5S include:

• Improves and sustains workplace organization.

• Develops and maintains a *visual workplace.*

- Provides the foundation for continuous improvement.

- Reduces clutter and the time it takes to look for tools and equipment.

- Improves how the operation appears to customers. The facility is always "tour ready."

- Creates pride in the workplace.

- Reduces "operator errors."

5S was a by-product of the Toyota Production System and is now a tool that is copied throughout North America and other developed countries. Most probably it was a system that was developed as a result of people doing a real good job at root cause analysis. In other words, instead of blaming a defect on an operator, Toyota engineers dug down deeper to find out why the operator made a defect and traced it back to poor organization in the workplace. They dug even deeper to ask why there was poor organization in the workplace and blamed the system, or the lack of a system. As a result, they developed 5S as the system to clean up and maintain the organization, which has the benefit of providing fewer opportunities for an employee to make mistakes. Even if this is not the way that 5S was first developed, I would like to think it happened this way, and it definitely *could* have happened this way.

Typically, 5S has been used in a shop environment. However, the use of 5S in less traditional environments such as offices and hospitals has been growing. I made a video called *Batchin'* in which I walked through the laundry process in my house, made a value stream map, and came up with many kaizen (improvement) activities to improve the process, which I still use today. One of the kaizen activities was to 5S my closet. In the process of *sorting,* I got rid of 161 pieces of clothing. For more information about this video, please visit www.mikemick.com.

F. SORTING THE QMS DOCUMENTATION

In *sort,* we physically identify items that are not used that often, have not been used for quite some time, or there are just too many being stored in the workplace of interest. Another term frequently used interchangeably with *sort* is *"red-tag"* because oftentimes we attach a red tag to the item in question and then move it out of the area being 5S'd. The red tag includes information to be recorded such as what the item is, why it's being red-tagged, and its final disposition after it has been moved out of the area of interest.

A simple online search for "red tag" will provide plenty of sources for purchasing these identifiers, if desired.

In a QMS documentation system, we *sort*, or red-tag, documents and document formats. Most often and initially, we concentrate on the highest two levels of the documentation system, the *quality manual* and *procedures*, though this same process can be applied to all types of documents, including work instructions, control plans, and forms.

The Two-Page Quality Manual

Oftentimes, when I work with a company to make recommendations on leaning out their documentation system I start with the highest-level document—the quality manual. Most quality manuals are anywhere from 25 to 70 pages in length. I've seen a few quality manuals greater than 100 pages in length. The quality manual paradigm that we must overcome, if we are so bold, is the belief that the organization's quality manual must mirror or duplicate the ISO 9001 standard. The quality manual *is* so long because we *do* mirror or duplicate the ISO 9001 standard, in our own words to some extent, and we end up with a document that is somewhat internally useless.

And yet, after the initial approval of the quality manual hardly anyone ever reads the quality manual with the exception of the management representative, an occasional overzealous internal auditor, and, of course, the registrar auditor (because he can charge you for his time to review the quality manual).

If virtually no one reads the quality manual, it is waste and is not adding value. If there is no value in the quality manual, we should red-tag it (perhaps literally move it to a temporary electronic folder entitled "Red Tag") and look to improve it so that it adds value. We red-tag it not because we want to get rid of it (nor can we for that matter), rather we want to get rid of most of it. The reason for red-tagging it is because we have too many non-value-added pages and words stored in a document we are required to maintain. Though there is value in having a quality manual, it is hard to find the value-added sections amongst all the non-value-added words and pages.

So why do we have a quality manual? ISO 9001 states that we shall have one, and it further defines what it must contain.

Section 4.2.2 of ISO 9001 states:

The organization shall establish and maintain a quality manual that includes

    a) the scope of the quality management system, including details of and justification for any exclusions,

b)   *the documented procedures established for the quality management system, or reference to them, and*

c)   *a description of the interaction between the processes of the quality management system.*

The scope of the QMS and the justification for exclusions as required in (a) can be written in one paragraph. Requirements (b) and (c) above can be accomplished with a flowchart of processes, in the form of documented procedures, showing their relationship and how they interact, on one page.

These requirements are easy to meet, which makes it possible to create a two-page quality manual that meets all ISO 9001 requirements, is user-friendly, and adds value to the entire organization. An example of an actual two-page quality manual is shown in Appendix D.

It must be stressed that what we are getting rid of is redundancy! The typical quality manual is, for the most part, restating the exact same requirements as in ISO 9001. The alternative is to not restate the requirements, state that the organization meets the requirements of ISO 9001, and create a hyperlink to the ISO 9001 standard from the quality manual.

Some organizations go the next step and place the two-page quality manual on each employee's desktop to be used as the portal into the quality management system. Anyone can get to a desired procedure through the quality manual with just two clicks of their mouse. Now, that's efficient and lean!

The Next Level—Procedures

Once again, a red tag folder is set up. A red tag folder is always meant to be temporary. In this case, we put wasteful or potentially wasteful documents in the folder with the idea in mind that a decision on the final disposition of each document placed in there will be made and determined within two weeks (or some agreed upon time period). The red tag folder must be deleted after that period of time! If it is not, we have just moved waste from one locale to another, similarly to your kids cleaning up their bedrooms by shoving all their stuff under the bed.

Now we must consider and determine what is meant by wasteful documents. Below are some guidelines that might be helpful.

Examples of Wasteful Procedures

1. Procedures that have not been revised for a long period of time (you determine what constitutes "a long period of time").

2. Procedures that have not been used for training employees for a long period of time.

3. Procedures that are informative only and do not really tell anybody what to do. In other words, there really is no procedure within the "procedure."

4. Procedures that are left over from ISO 9001:1994, including those with titles such as:

   a. Management responsibility

   b. Quality system

   c. Control of customer-supplied product

   d. Product identification and traceability

   e. Inspection and test status

   f. Handling, storage, packaging, preservation, and delivery

   g. Statistical techniques

   This is not to say that there is not valuable information in some of these documents. However, the valuable information is probably already located in a different procedure or work instruction. These are most probably redundant with other documents.

5. Procedures that are just a bunch of mumbo-jumbo and do not really affect the quality of the product, service, or process. Some of these procedures are written just like the ISO 9001 standard and mean nothing to the employees.

6. Procedures that are redundant with other documents.

7. Procedures that are really work instructions (steps performed by *one* person or department).

Occasionally, I will find procedures that fall into multiple categories. In a conference room with the employees of a medical device manufacturer in California, we were looking into their electronic folder containing all of their procedures. The folder was projected onto a screen with an LCD projector. I looked down the list and chuckled to myself when I saw the procedure called "Statistical Techniques." I told the group that I would bet that procedure had not been revised since they were certified 10 years prior. We opened it up and I was found to be wrong. It was revised once, about eight years prior, when the company name changed. This procedure, besides being a holdover from the '94 standard and not being revised for many years, was also written as a bunch of mumbo-jumbo that really had no effect on the quality of products, services, and processes.

Sometimes, when I am working within a client's facility and assessing their quality management system to make recommendations, the client may get a little jittery about having an outsider moving documents around in their network. In this case, I will then make an electronic copy of their list of procedures and add columns such as "Actions to Take" and "Reason for Action." Possible "actions to take" would be:

1. Eliminate this document

2. Combine with another specified document

3. Downsize

4. Get rid of sections that are in other documents

5. Make into a work instruction (or form or database)

6. Rewrite to address . . .

One example of a procedure that was just a bunch of mumbo-jumbo and meant nothing to the employees is the resource management procedure in Figure 2.1.

This was a real procedure in a real company that was certified for many years to QS-9000. I came in to help them convert to ISO/TS 16949. They had only changed "QS-9000" to "ISO/TS 16949" and felt like they were done. Every procedure was written in the same format and had the same value. The shame of the situation was that this company had a documentation system that was of no value and yet they were still certified! The problems with this procedure were many, including:

1. The procedure had little to do with resource management.

2. There is no flow. It is written like the standard.

3. It covered topics such as document types and customer surveys, which have nothing to do with resource management.

4. Responsibilities are missing.

5. It's mumbo-jumbo that has no meaning.

This is a procedure that I red-tagged and stated that the action to be taken would be to rewrite the procedure in process flow fashion and address the hiring, training, and ensuring of competency of all employees. In fact, for this client I rewrote the procedure based on what they actually did and addressed the requirements that were missing from their process, then used

ABC Manufacturing	
Operational Procedure	6. Resource Management

6. *Resource Management Provision of Resources.* ABC maintains a documented quality management system as a means to ensure that all products and services conform to specified requirements. The following four levels of documentation are utilized and maintained to meet the requirements of ISO: 9001/TS16949 and other customer-specific manuals and procedures are incorporated into the four-level documented quality systems as required per the contract review process.

- Quality Manual

- Quality System Procedures

- Work Instructions (define activity performed)

- Quality Records (provide evidence of results)

The Sales department conducts surveys of customers. Customers are then asked to respond to survey questions pertaining to products and performance of ABC. The frequency and manner of these surveys depend on specific arrangements with particular customers.

6.2 *Human Resources*

6.2.1 *General.* ABC qualifies personnel on the basis of appropriate education, training, and experience.

6.2.2 *Competence, Awareness, and Training.* ABC determines the necessary competence needed to perform specific jobs. Managers perform formal employee reviews annually to determine if the employee's competence is satisfactory or if they need to be developed further with additional training. When it is determined that training is needed, training is provided by qualified sources. Records are kept in accordance with the procedure for Control of Quality Records.

6.2.2.1 *Product Design Skills.* The organization is not responsible for product design at this time.

6.2.2.2 *Training.* Managers have the authority to identify training needs that will satisfy all activities affecting product quality and customer requirements.

Originator: General Nothing	Revision 1	1
Date: 1/15/04	Approved date: 1/15/04	

Figure 2.1   Real procedure from a former QS-9000 certified company.

ABC Manufacturing	
Operational Procedure	6. Resource Management

6.2.2.3 *Training on the job.* The responsible manager identifies the need for on-the-job training Personnel who have demonstrated satisfactory job performance will be reviewed for competence and awareness. Records of training are maintained.

6.2.2.4 *Employee motivation and empowerment.* Reference procedure 6.2.2.4

6.3 *Infrastructure.* ABC provides the necessary tools, equipment, and workspace to meet product requirements

6.3.1 *Plant facility and equipment planning.* Top management evaluates facility floor space for best equipment and material flow.

6.3.2 *Contingency plan.* ABC has prepared a contingency plan to reasonably protect the customer's supply in the event of an emergency such as: utility interruptions, labor shortages, and failure of key equipment and field returns. (See contingency plan).

6.4 *Work environment.* ABC maintains a work environment that is conducive to meeting product requirements.

6.4.1 *Personnel safety to achieve product quality.* A safety coordinator is appointed to be the company's representative to minimize potential risks and to comply with environmental regulations.

The safety coordinator determines which governmental regulations apply to the organization and implements the appropriate systems to ensure compliance.

6.4.2 *Cleanliness of premises.* ABCs maintains the production areas to be clean, safe and a suitable working environment for all employees.

Originator: General Nothing	Revision 1	2
Date: 1/15/04	Approved date: 1/15/04	

Figure 2.1   *Continued.*

the before and after documents as a training tool for their employees, so that *they* knew how to transform their documents.

Another example, in Figure 2.2, is of a procedure that I recommended eliminating because it really stated nothing unique from what would have already been located in other procedures. It was a holdover procedure from the 1994 edition of ISO 9001 and it was entitled "Control of Customer-Supplied Product." Also, note that the last update occurred in 2002. I reviewed this company's QMS in 2009. You may see my notes at the end of each paragraph regarding why each sentence was not necessary and why, overall, the document could be eliminated. The other recommendation I made was to modify the "Scope" section of a couple of other procedures (for example, Receiving Inspection and Testing) to include customer-supplied product.

G. SORTING WITHIN PROCEDURES

After red-tagging procedures, it is a good idea to have the employees red-tag the content and standardized sections of the procedures for waste. I usually purchase red adhesive arrows and after a brief training session have individuals red-tag a procedure such as the one in Figure 2.3, discuss it, and then red-tag one of their own procedures. We must first consider and determine what is meant by wasteful content within procedures. Below are some guidelines that might be helpful.

Examples of Wasteful Content within Procedures

1. Sections that are not read by the users. Watch people approve, review, and/or read procedures, and/or train other people in procedures and observe whether they skip over certain sections. Ask people what they read and do not read.

2. Paragraphs in which the content is already located in other documents. Oftentimes, if a company does not make a clear distinction between a procedure and work instruction, the same information will be repeated in both. Also, there might often be a document that defines all the parts on the form to be completed. This is another form of redundancy. Just state, "complete the form" or "complete Section 2 of the form," or record the requirement on the form itself (that is, "Section 2: [To be completed by initiator]). The key is to improve the form to make it self-explanatory.

XYZ Systems, Inc.

Controlled document if printed on XYZ quality paper.

Control of Customer-Supplied Product

Purpose

The purpose of this procedure is to define the control of Customer-Supplied Product within our Quality System. It shall be the responsibility of the V.P. of Operations to ensure that this procedure is implemented and followed.

Definitions

Customer-Supplied Product   Any item(s) supplied by the customer for use in the production of product for later delivery to the same customer. *(Duh.)*

Procedure

1.0 *General*

    1.1   It shall be the responsibility of all employees to control, with reasonable care, all product supplied by the customer. *(This really says nothing.)*

    1.2   Any such product that is lost, damaged, or is otherwise unsuitable for use shall be recorded and reported to the customer. *(By whom? On what? Redundant with step 2.3 below. This is just copying the words of the standard.)*

    1.3   Verification by the supplier does not absolve the customer of the responsibility to provide acceptable product. *(Same thing—copied from the standard. Informative.)*

2.0 *Verification*

    2.1   All incoming customer-supplied product will be processed under the Receiving Inspection program. See Receiving Inspection and Testing (QUA 04). *(It's in that procedure—no need to reference.)*

    2.2   All customer-supplied product identified as nonconforming shall be dispositioned according to the Nonconforming Material Procedure (QUA 01). *(It's in that procedure—no need to reference.)*

    2.3   Upon receipt from the customer, all units will be checked for visual damage and to verify that a green test dot has been affixed

---

Revision no.: 05   OPS 05
Issue date: 7/12/02   Page: 1 of 2

Figure 2.2   Useless and wasteful procedure.

XYZ Systems, Inc

Controlled document if printed on XYZ quality paper.

---

to the hour meter. The green dot verifies that the unit has completed test and that the test sheets have been placed inside the connection box. Any discrepancies will be reported to the customer. *(This is already defined in the Receiving Inspection and Testing procedure.)*

2.4   Prior to final assembly of units, operators will verify that:

     2.4.1   The generator frame has a bar code showing the model number, serial number, and order number.

     2.4.2   The data plate on the unit matches all the information on the data plate stamp on the stand by special instruction sheet (yellow sheet). *(Already located in the Process Control procedure.)*

3.0   *Storage and Maintenance*

     3.1   All customer-supplied products shall be stored and maintained according to Material Handling, Storage, Packaging, Preservation and Delivery (OPS 13). *(Stated elsewhere in other procedures.)*

Revision History
Author: Michael

Rev. no.	Issue date	Changes made	Initiator(s)	Approved by	Date approved
0	09/03/98	New procedure.			08/27/98
01	11/06/98	Added 2.1.1 and 2.1.2, what operator checks upon receiving customer supplied units. Added 2.3 and 2.4 to include inspection of units upon receipt from customer and prior to assembly.			11/02/98
02	12/14/98	2.2 Added "All discrepancies will be reported to the customer." 2.3 and 2.4 were deleted.			12/08/98
03	06/23/99	Deleted 2.1.1, 2.1.2, 2.1.2.1, 2.1.2.2, and 2.1.2.3. Same as 2.3, 2.4, 2.4.1, 2.4.2, and 2.4.3.			06/25/99
04	09/03/99	Deleted 2.4.1. Added what the green dot verifies to section 2.3.			09/03/99
05	07/12/02	Changed "Director" to "V.P."			07/10/02

Revision no.: 05	OPS 05
Issue date: 7/12/02	Page: 2 of 2

Figure 2.2   *Continued.*

Title: Process Control for Housing Manufacturing	Procedure no: IG-014-2
~~Distribution:~~ ~~1) Plant information center 3) Human resources~~ ~~2) Plant manager 4) Purchasing~~ ~~5) ID (not necessary)~~	Revision Level: 8 Date: 06/13/2002
	Page: 1 of 9
	Origin date: 08/11/95

Approved: _____

                              Department Manager

~~Author:~~

Change Record			
Rev. level	Date initiated	Person responsible	Description of change
~~6~~	~~02/20/2001~~	~~??~~	~~Revise 4.3, 4.6, 6.1.2, and 6.11. Delete references to forms 030-001-4 and 030-009-4. Add 5.13 (010-073-3), and 6.1.19.~~
~~7~~	~~11/14/2001~~	~~??~~	~~Added Form # 740-042-4 in Section 4.3~~
8	06/13/2002	??	Revised 3.5: CP rev. by date. Corrected 5.12: Form #. Revised 6.1.15: Inventory tags as backup for barcode. Revised 6.5.3: Coolant maintenance and monitoring. Deleted 7.1: Retention of form 010-010-4. Deleted 7.2: Retention of hard copies of process routings. Revised 7.3: Electronic filing of changes to routings. Added 7.6: Retaining setup approval sheets.
			(Move to back, only keep last Rev. history since documents are being archived)

User Checklist

	1. Accounting		11. Manufacturing special project
	2. Assembly	X	12. Material control
	3. Design	X	13. Production administration
	4. Engineering		14. Purchasing
	5. HR/Training	X	15. Quality systems
	6. Logistics		16. I-D
	7. M.I.S.		17. Service
X	8. Maintenance		18. Supplier quality
X	9. Manufacturing		19. Tool room
X	10. Manufacturing quality	X	20. Off highway (Not necessary)

~~730-020-4, Rev. 3~~   Valid controlled copy only if red stamp is present

Figure 2.3   Red-lined procedure (before leaning out).

Title: Process Control for Housing Manufacturing	Procedure no: IG-014-2
~~Distribution:~~ ~~1) Plant information center 3) Human resources~~ ~~2) Plant manager 4) Purchasing~~ ~~5) ID (not necessary)~~	**Revision** **Level: 8** **Date:** 06/13/2002
	Page: 2 of 9
	Origin date: 08/11/95

1.0 *Purpose.* To ensure that processes are carried out under controlled conditions in order to maintain satisfactory compliance with quality standards and to improve the effectiveness of process operations ~~per QS-9000 Element 4.9.~~

2.0 *Scope.* This procedure applies to all parts and functions involved in the manufacturing processes for housings within department 10.

~~3.0 Definitions of terms. *(Define within the document)*~~

~~3.1 CMM: Coordinate measuring machine~~

~~3.2 CNC-Program: alpha numeric machine instructions for a computer numeric controlled equipment to perform defined functions in a repetitive automatic process.~~

~~3.4 MSDS: Material safety data sheet~~

~~3.5 Quality control plan: When product engineering includes/specific special characteristics (key product, significant, main and/or critical), manufacturing engineering will include these characteristics as a part of their process control plan, per the APQP manual. The plans are part number specific and provide process control, documentation requirements, and methods to assure integrity of finished product per design output 004-2. Change revision levels are defined by date. Changes are recorded and filed at the page bottom electronically for the life of the documents. As applicable enhanced control plans will be used from start-up through 90 days into production then removed.~~

~~3.6 CMM-Protocol: Inspection protocol written by a coordinate measuring machine.~~

~~3.7 Production plan: used for setting production schedules as assigned by material control.~~

~~3.8 Process routing: Document to describe the proper method of producing components in the shop.~~

~~3.9 PM: Preventive maintenance~~

~~730 020 4, Rev. 3~~

Figure 2.3 *Continued.*

Title: Process Control for Housing Manufacturing	Procedure no: IG-014-2
~~Distribution:~~ ~~1) Plant information center~~ ~~3) Human resources~~ ~~2) Plant manager~~ ~~4) Purchasing~~ ~~5) ID (not necessary)~~	**Revision** **Level: 8** **Date:** 06/13/2002 **Page:** 3 of 9 **Origin date:** 08/11/95

~~3.10 Operator daily production report: Monitors machine down time and operator efficiency by work center on a 24 hr. basis. Operator record components produced and log down time identified by code and amount of time lost.~~

~~3.11 SPC: Statistical process control~~

~~4.0 Responsibilities.~~ *(Define within procedure)*

~~Responsibilities include but are not limited to:~~

~~4.1 Department manager: oversees all processes to ensure conformance to control standards.~~

~~4.2 Supervisors: shop floor coordination, control manpower assignments, production scheduling, maintenance scheduling of machine repair.~~

~~4.3 Floaters: machine set up, production output, component quality, conduct operator training and document operator training on work instruction change form (740-051-4) or training roster (740-042-4), support operators with machine adjustments.~~

~~4.4 Operators: machine set up, production, preventive maintenance, statistical process control, in process quality inspection, machine adjustments control documentation.~~

~~4.5 Manufacturing engineers: manufacturing processes, manufacturing improvements, tooling and fixturing, performance to standards, support and assist management, supply and coordinate systems for daily tracking and notify production supervisor about changes in work instructions.~~

~~4.6 CNC programmer: CNC programming, process optimization, assist machine operators with programming and quality problems.~~

~~4.7 Gage room: CMM inspection (in process, setup and prototype production parts), manual part inspection of setup parts, surface roughness inspection.~~

~~4.8 Manufacturing quality: preliminary and ongoing process capability studies.~~

~~4.9 Maintenance: Perform preventive maintenance (PM).~~

~~730-020-4, Rev. 3~~

Figure 2.3   *Continued.*

Title: Process Control for Housing Manufacturing	Procedure no: IG-014-2
~~Distribution:~~ ~~1) Plant information center 3) Human resources~~ ~~2) Plant manager 4) Purchasing~~ ~~5) ID (not necessary)~~	Revision Level: 8 Date: 06/13/2002
	Page: 4 of 9
	Origin date: 08/11/95

~~5.0   References.~~ *(In procedure)*

~~5.1   ID-004-2   Design output~~

~~5.2   IG-012-2   Request for manufacturing deviation~~

~~5.3   IG-027-2   Preventive maintenance procedure~~

~~5.4   042-2   Nonconforming product~~

~~5.5   010-010-4   Daily production report sheet~~

~~5.6   010-011-4   Control forms~~

~~5.7   010-030-3   Master book of work instructions~~

~~5.8   010-068-4   Setup approval sheet~~

~~5.9   010-079-4   Operator quality check list~~

~~5.10 740-051-4   Work instruction change form~~

~~5.11 010-053-3   Setup instructions~~

~~5.12 010-073-3   Housing inspection after process interruption~~

6.0   Procedure.

6.1   The shift supervisors hand out work assignments based on a production schedule/plan.

6.2   Operators perform activities according to process routings, process flow charts, control plans, operator checklists, part prints, and supporting work instructions, which are located in the machining department.

6.3   The machine operator, floater, and/or a setup team performs machine setups according to machine setup instructions (010-053-3) and the latest version of the CNC program stored in the machine controller.

6.4   The operator machines initial setup parts and inspects them according to quality control plan and submits the parts to the Inspector.

~~730-020-4, Rev. 3~~

Figure 2.3   *Continued.*

Title: Process Control for Housing Manufacturing	Procedure no: IG-014-2
~~Distribution:~~ ~~1) Plant information center 3) Human resources~~ ~~2) Plant manager 4) Purchasing~~ ~~5) ID (not necessary)~~	Revision Level: 8 Date: 06/13/2002
	Page: 5 of 9
	Origin date: 08/11/95

6.5   The inspector inspects the first piece in accordance with the control plan, records the results on the setup approval sheet (Form 010-068-4) and discusses the results with the operator.

6.6   If necessary, the machine operator adjusts the machining operations based on the inspection results.

6.7   Once acceptable, the inspector, team leader, and operator sign the setup approval sheet (Form 010-068-4).

~~6.8~~   The machine operator machines parts and performs in process inspection using product-specific control plan. ~~Inspection results are recorded in the operator quality checklist (010-079-4).~~ (located in Control Plan)

~~6.1.9~~   ~~If Product Design Engineering includes specific characteristics (key product, significant, main and/or critical) then these characteristics are indicated in the quality control plan.~~ (located in Design Change Procedure)

6.1.10   ~~Machine operator submits parts for in process CMM inspection to Gage Room. Control plans specify frequency and quantity of parts to be submitted to Gageroom for CMM inspection.~~ *(Repeated and in control plan)*

~~6.1.11~~   (in Control of Nonconforming Product Procedure) ~~Parts that can be reworked to meet specification will be reworked immediately, inspected, and will be supplied back in to production. If these parts can not be reworked immediately they will be quarantined until they can be reworked.~~

~~Suspect parts are tagged with a Quarantine Tag (720-016-4) and stored in the quarantine cage until they are reviewed and dispositioned. Due to the size of the housings it is possible that nonconforming or suspect parts must be quarantined outside the cage. In this case the quarantined parts must be clearly separated from conforming parts.~~

~~730-020-4, Rev. 3~~

Figure 2.3   *Continued.*

Title: Process Control for Housing Manufacturing	Procedure no: IG-014-2
~~Distribution:~~ ~~1) Plant information center 3) Human resources~~ ~~2) Plant manager 4) Purchasing~~ ~~5) ID (not necessary)~~	**Revision** **Level: 8** **Date:** 06/13/2002
	Page: 6 of 9
	Origin date: 08/11/95

~~Parts that can not be reworked and can not be approved per Manufacturing Deviation, will be placed into the MRB Holding area for the MRB review and disposition (042-2).~~

~~As required, the supervisor on duty can initiate the running of Non-conforming products and quarantine material with DMN until disposition is made per Request for Manufacturing Deviation (012-2).~~

~~Parts that are not to specification, can not be released into production without approved manufacturing deviation.~~

~~6.1.12~~   ~~Manufacturing Quality performs preliminary and ongoing process capability studies.~~ *(Control plans—next step also)*

~~6.1.13~~   ~~Machine operators collect SPC data where applicable.~~

6.1.18   If the process is interrupted, machine operators follow the Housing Inspection after Process Interruption Work Instruction (010-073-3).

6.1.19   If there is an equipment problem, operators must immediately report it to the Maintenance Department.

6.1.20   After the parts are complete, the Material Handler transports the product to the washing operation in accordance with the Inventory Control Procedure (002-2).

6.1.15   The Washing Operator stacks all finished parts on transportation pallets and tags the pallets with bar code labels (where do these come from?). Inventory tags are used as backups for the bar code system.

6.1.21   All operators complete Daily Production Reports (Form 010-010-4) at the end of their shift.

6.1.22   All operators perform Preventive Maintenance in accordance with the Preventive Maintenance Procedure (011-2).

~~730 020 4, Rev. 3~~

Figure 2.3   *Continued.*

Title: Process Control for Housing Manufacturing	Procedure no: IG-014-2
~~Distribution:~~ ~~1) Plant information center 3) Human resources~~ ~~2) Plant manager 4) Purchasing~~ ~~5) ID (not necessary)~~	Revision Level: 8 Date: 06/13/2002
	Page: 7 of 9
	Origin date: 08/11/95

> 6.1.23 Manufacturing Quality inputs SPC data into the SPC software, monitors Cpk values, initiates the Corrective and Preventive Action Procedure (017-2) when Cpk values fall below customer requirements and notifies the customer if process capability can not be restored

~~6.2   Production Equipment:~~

> ~~6.2.1   Owners and maintenance manuals for production equipment are kept by the maintenance department.~~ *(Located in PM procedure)*

> ~~6.2.1   Performance and accuracy of production equipment is constantly monitored through the regular inspection of parts processed by the equipment.~~

> ~~6.2.3   Any changes to the process (Engineering, Material, Production Environment) require engineering and/or management approval.~~ *(Located in PPAP procedure)*

~~6.3   Production Environment:~~

> ~~6.3.1   The housekeeping and organization of production areas is emphasized by management as an important requirement for safety and quality.~~ *(No value—same with next sentence)*

> ~~6.3.2   Personnel report conditions such as inadequate ventilation, excessive high or low temperatures, poor lighting, and other problems that adversely affect safety / production.~~

> ~~6.3.3   Management teams regularly survey the production areas to help identify problems with improperly stored material, products, tools and items outside designated storage areas. These teams have the authority to request clearing and cleanup of production and storage areas at anytime.~~ *(Not true—internal auditing)*

~~6.4   Preventive Maintenance is addressed in procedure 027-2 Preventive Maintenance.~~ *(Stated above)*

~~730 020 4, Rev. 3~~

Figure 2.3   *Continued.*

Title: Process Control for Housing Manufacturing	Procedure no: IG-014-2
~~Distribution:~~ ~~1) Plant information center~~ ~~3) Human resources~~ ~~2) Plant manager~~ ~~4) Purchasing~~ ~~5) ID (not necessary)~~	**Revision Level: 8** **Date:** 06/13/2002 **Page:** 8 of 9 **Origin date:** 08/11/95

6.5 ~~Disposal of Production Supplies:~~ (located in environmental procedure)

   ~~6.5.1   All chemicals and production supplying materials that are involved in the housing manufacturing process and operation of the equipment, such as coolant and lubricating material, are in compliance with government safety regulations.~~

   ~~6.5.2   MSDS are located in specially identified areas and are accessible to all employees. A complete list of all materials used for preventive maintenance is kept at each machine.~~

   ~~6.5.3   The coolant used in the machining equipment is continuously being refreshed and filtered in a central coolant system. Its concentration is inspected via refractometer and maintained by the shift floaters. The quality of the coolant is monitored by the supplier. On a monthly basis samples are taken for laboratory analysis. Laboratory reports are filed electronically and distributed to the housing supervisor.~~

   ~~6.5.4   Until disposal, all waste oil is stored in tanks outside the plant. The waste material is frequently picked up by an approved source for disposal of waste.~~

   ~~Additional specific information is provided in Solid Waste Disposal Program.~~

~~6.6   Process Capability~~ (located in PPAP)~~—Prior to the release of any product into production a pre-production build is preformed in order for the quality and manufacturing departments to verify that equipment and process have the capability for producing a quality product.~~

   ~~6.6.1   Initial process capability as determined at the time of PPAP will be used as the baseline for ongoing capability performance.~~

~~730 020 4, Rev. 3~~

Figure 2.3 *Continued.*

Title: Process Control for Housing Manufacturing	Procedure no: IG-014-2
~~Distribution:~~ ~~1) Plant information center 3) Human resources~~ ~~2) Plant manager 4) Purchasing~~ ~~5) ID (not necessary)~~	**Revision** **Level: 8** **Date:** 06/13/2002
	Page: 9 of 9
	Origin date: 08/11/95

~~6.7   Contingency Plans: The company will prepare and maintain contingency plans to reasonably protect the supply of component parts for assembly to the customer in the event of an emergency.~~
(Contingency plan)

7.0   ~~Records:~~ *(Located In Control of Quality Records procedure)*

~~7.1   deleted~~

~~7.2   deleted~~

~~7.3   Records of changes to process routing are filed electronically.~~

~~7.4   Hardcopies of process routings for obsolete parts are stored in manufacturing engineering department for a minimum of 5 years after last part was produced.~~

~~7.5   Completed operator quality checklists are filed in the manufacturing engineering department for a minimum of 1 calendar year after the year the record was created.~~

~~7.6   Setup Approval Sheets (Form 010-068-4) are retained in the Gage Room for a minimum of one calendar year after records are created.~~

~~730-020-4, Rev. 3~~

Figure 2.3   *Continued.*

3. Informative sections or paragraphs that really do not tell anyone to do anything.

4. Redundant sections. This could include having content repeated in both flowchart form and text form within the same document.

5. Batching of topics throughout the procedure rather than writing in process flow fashion.

6. Batching of information in sections rather than just presenting the information in the procedure in process flow fashion. These "batch" sections may include:

   a. General (as in Figure 2.2)

   b. Responsibilities

   c. References

   d. Exhibits

   e. Definitions

   f. Policy

   In other words, why have a separate section called "Responsibilities" when the responsibility of each action should be defined throughout the procedure? Why have a separate section called "References" when throughout the procedure one should be citing the references? Why have a separate section called "Definitions" when words, acronyms, or vocabulary should be defined as they are used within the procedure? In other words, record "Responsibilities," "References," "Definitions" in single-piece flow as they are used—much like lean would tell us to do—not in batches.

   It's natural to batch things of a similar nature together, and this holds true for the content within documents, but for the most part this is wasteful. If references are referred to in the body of a procedure and then again summarized as a group of References, it is redundant. I challenge any company whose documents include a References section (or one of the other sections listed above) to compare all the documents that are referred to throughout one sample document of your choice to the list of references. There will always be multiple documents referred to throughout the procedure that are *not* located on the summary list called References, and there will always be documents listed in the

References section that are *not* referred to in the body of the procedure. This is inherent any time there is a redundancy of information.

Batching of information within documents (and between documents) is redundant and wasteful.

In Figure 2.3, another real (eight-page) procedure from a real company is shown, before the leaning out process. The document shown has been "red-lined," an acceptable variation to red-tagging, along with brief explanations in parentheses as to why the sections were red-lined.

Note to the reader. The numbering in the actual main body of the procedure shown in Figure 2.3 is confusing and wrong. This is the way it was written in the actual document.

In Figure 2.4, I show the leaned out procedure, which went from eight pages down to 1.5 pages just by eliminating the redundancy, and not eliminating any important content. The reader should know that the focus was not necessarily on improving the content of the procedure itself, rather it was only on eliminating the redundancy. In other words, there still could be more improvements made to the remaining content.

It is not uncommon to experience a 50 to 80 percent reduction in the overall number of pages in a QMS by going through a leaning out process as described in this chapter. This example shows this type of reduction, without eliminating important content.

If all the recommendations were taken, the procedure would look like Figure 2.4.

H. INTERNAL AUDITORS CAN HELP SORT

The ideal lean quality system will never repeat a requirement, specification, or activity step. The quality system, through excellent references, user-friendly document numbering system, links, and hyperlinks, should flow well and should be lean.

A quality system that repeats requirements, and so on, will eventually result in errors because as improvements and changes are made, one document will be changed and the other(s) will not, creating inconsistencies and nonconformities.

While performing internal audits, auditors can:

I. Look for redundant statements, specifications, and requirements:

A. Within a document

Title: Process Control for Housing Manufacturing	**Proc. no:** IG-014-2
Revision: Level 8 Date: 06/13/02	**Page:** 1 of 2

1.0   *Purpose.* To ensure that processes are carried out under controlled conditions in order to maintain satisfactory compliance with quality standards and to improve the effectiveness of process operations.

2.0   *Scope.* This procedure applies to all parts and functions involved in the manufacturing processes for housings within department 10.

This procedure covers from the completion of the Incoming Inspection and Testing procedure (IG-006-2) to the initiation of the Process Control-Assembly procedure (IG-088-2).

3.0   *Procedure.*

3.1   The shift supervisors hand out work assignments based on a production schedule/plan.

3.2   Operators perform activities according to process routings, process flowcharts, control plans, operator checklists, part prints, and supporting work instructions, which are located in the machining department.

3.3   The machine operator, floater, and/or a setup team performs machine setups according to Machine Setup Instructions (Form 010-053-3) and the latest version of the CNC program stored in the machine controller.

3.4   The operator machines initial setup parts and inspects them according to Quality Control Plan and submits the parts to the inspector.

3.5   The inspector inspects the first piece in accordance with the Control Plan, records the results on the Setup Approval Sheet (Form 010-068-4) and discusses the results with the operator.

3.6   If necessary, the machine operator adjusts the machining operations based on the inspection results.

3.7   Once acceptable, the inspector, team leader, and operator sign the Setup Approval Sheet (Form 010-068-4).

3.8   The machine operator machines parts and performs in-process inspection using product-specific Control Plan.

3.9   If the process is interrupted, machine operators follow the Housing Inspection after Process Interruption Work Instruction (Form 010-073-3).

3.10   If there is an equipment problem, operators must immediately report it to the maintenance department.

730 020 4, Rev. 3

Figure 2.4   Procedure after leaning out.

Title: Process Control for Housing Manufacturing	Proc. no: IG-014-2
Revision: Level 8 Date: 06/13/02	Page: 2 of 2

3.11 After the parts are complete, the material handler transports the product to the washing operation in accordance with the Inventory Control procedure (002-2).

3.12 The washing operator stacks all finished parts on transportation pallets and tags the pallets with bar code labels. Inventory tags are used as backups for the bar code system.

3.13 All operators complete Daily Production Reports (Form 010-010-4) at the end of their shift.

3.14 All operators perform preventive maintenance in accordance with the Preventive Maintenance procedure (011-2).

3.15 Manufacturing quality inputs SPC data into the SPC software, monitors C_{pk} values, initiates the Corrective and Preventive Action procedure (017-2) when C_{pk} values fall below customer requirements, and notifies the customer if process capability can not be restored.

Change Record			
Rev. level	Date initiated	Approval	Description of change
8	06/13/2002	Department manager	Revised 3.5: CP rev. by date. Corrected 5.12: Form #. Revised 6.1.15: Inventory tags as backup for bar code. Revised 6.5.3: Coolant maintenance and monitoring. Deleted 7.1: Retention of form 010-010-4. Deleted 7.2: Retention of hardcopies of process routings. Revised 7.3: Electronic filing of changes to routings. Added 7.6: Retaining setup approval sheets.

730 020 4, Rev. 3

Figure 2.4   *Continued.*

160 pages remaining *(31.6% read)*

1. Search for the same topics being addressed in different sections of the same document (that is, within the procedure and within a different section like "Responsibilities" or "References").

2. Be aware of procedures or work instructions that do not flow fluidly from one paragraph to the next and create a hand-off of information, product, paper, or knowledge, either manually or electronically. When not written sequentially, the writer has a tendency to replicate the same requirements throughout the document.

B. Between documents

1. Look for the same activities being addressed at different levels of documents.

    a. Oftentimes, a procedure will refer to a work instruction, and the work instruction will repeat much of the same information that is in the procedure.

    b. Oftentimes, a procedure or work instruction will require a person to complete specific sections on a form and will list those sections (that is, "the inspector records the nonconformity, date, name, possible cause on the form"). If you check the form itself, it may have been changed and no longer contains those sections. Instead, it should state, "complete the form" or "complete Section II of the form."

2. Look for the same activities being addressed in different types of documents (that is, procedures, flowcharts, control plans, specification sheets, forms, electronic documents, drawings).

II. Look for repeated customer or internal numeric specifications.

A. Oftentimes, a numeric dimension or functional specification is repeated many times, and it is very easy to find inconsistencies, especially if there has been a change. Dimensions or functional requirements can be repeated from customer prints/specifications to internal prints/specifications, control plans, travelers, work orders, work instructions, inspection sheets, SPC charts, quality alerts, and so on.

III. Look for redundancies in contractual documents with suppliers and customers including the contract, purchase order, referenced terms and conditions, supplier quality manuals, referenced specifications, order acknowledgments, and prints.

IV. Search for words that do not tell a person what to do. There should be one well-written "Purpose" statement at the beginning of a procedure. There is no reason for explanations, justifications, or philosophy after that section.

V. Be watchful for replications, and when discovered, audit that process or part of the process and record a nonconformity, if observed, or an opportunity for improvement (OFI)/preventive action.

Examples of Wasteful Forms Needing Sorting

The following examples of wasteful forms will be discussed at different points in this book. Any of these could have been observed by internal auditors:

1. One company had two facilities in Texas and Tennessee. Between the two facilities, we counted 11 different problem-solving forms that all required root cause analysis.

2. One company had a Waste Walk form for their lean-minded people that looked very similar to their Corrective/Preventive Action form for their ISO-minded people.

3. Many companies have multiple Internal Audit forms that require the same information to be recorded several times.

I. SETTING THE QMS DOCUMENTATION IN ORDER

Setting in order is the next step in the 5S process. The idea behind this step is that everything should have its own place. If something is missing, it is obvious. In the physical manufacturing world, this includes having shadow boards (that identify by shadows or outlines the exact shape and location of each important item), visual management and control, and color coding. One purpose of setting in order is to make sure that whatever is required to do the job, it is easy to get to in as few steps as possible.

But what does setting in order means in the world of QMS documentation?

1. Documents must be easy to get to and easy to find with as few pages to turn or as few clicks of the mouse as possible. This is the advantage of having the quality manual on each person's desktop to serve as the portal into the entire QMS. Of course, the use of hyperlinks to get to one document from another is a great tool because it only takes one mouse click to get to the hyperlinked document.

2. All documents must be referred to by at least one other document. If someone introduces a brand-new work instruction, there must be another document referring to it.

3. In the manufacturing world or any environment that has a work order, shop order, control plan, or traveler that follows the job, it is best to have these documents refer to the actual work instruction needed for each activity called out on the document itself.

4. If maintaining some number of hard-copy documents, keep only the documents needed in a specific area in that area. Do not put all documents in all places. This makes it difficult to find the documents needed. The same goes for electronic documents. Group all documents (that is, procedures, work instructions, forms) in a folder by process, rather than type of document, and include only those required for that process.

5. If using document numbers (which are not required), give them a logical numbering system and link the documents vertically. As an example, the corrective/preventive action procedure could be given a number like 8.5-01 (8.5 is the relevant section in the ISO 9001 standard). If this procedure references a work instruction, give it a number like 8.5-01-01 (the extra set of digits represents a work instruction). If this work instruction references a form, give the form a number like 8.5-01-01A, where the letter at the end represents a form. This way, it's easy to trace back to the referencing document at any level.

6. In the spirit of lean, it should be very easy to get to the most often used documents. They should be "out there" where the work is, and they should have pictures, photos, and color coordination so that it is easy to find certain sections within documents.

7. Arrange files and folders by usage, not types of documents. In many organizations, there is a Procedures folder that contains all procedures, a Work Instructions folder that contains all work instructions, and so on. This is an example of not setting up the

folders in a process-oriented way that would make it easier for the
user of the documents,

8. Ensure that file names make it easy for the user to find documents.
   Oftentimes, companies develop a file name structure that starts
   off with document numbers, which are then naturally arranged
   alphanumerically within the system. For most users, this is not
   user-friendly because they do not know the numbering system.
   They would find it easier to search alphanumerically by words
   in the title of the document rather than some obscure numbers.
   It would be best to name a file "Brake Motor Order Entry" rather
   than "AA 7.2.1-014 Brake Motor Order Entry."

An example of using 5S, especially *set in order*, to improve the order entry
process is found in Chapter 4, section C, "5S'ing Files and Folders (A Lean
Order Entry Case Study).

J. SHINING THE QMS DOCUMENTATION

Shine is about keeping the area and machinery clean and orderly. It's also
about inspecting the area and machinery, while cleaning it, against a set of
known criteria as a means of identifying a potential problem ahead of time
and doing something about it prior to it becoming a problem. Shine should
also have a preventive aspect to it that promotes the design of equipment,
machinery, systems, or an area to prevent dirtiness and disorderliness from
occurring.

How does *shine* apply to QMS documentation?

1. Putting systems and provisions in place to ensure that documents
   are clearly legible, especially if they are hung in a shop
   environment. This may include lamination and/or plastic sleeves.

2. Make sure hard copies of documents are posted in such a way that
   they are easily readable (correct height, located by the work, no
   curled edges due to humidity or a poor posting methodology).

3. Use plenty of photographs and color, in the spirit of lean.

4. Use visual standards of what's good and what's bad.

5. Ensure that document control features mandated by ISO 9001
   are also applied to lean documents (that is, leader standard

work, combination work sheets, 5S assessment forms, job breakdown sheets). This includes revision control, approvals, and a revision record.

6. Look outside of the current QMS (for example, shipping area) for documents that should be controlled but are not (memos, sticky notes, e-mails, customer-supplied documents, and so on).

7. Look for documents representing what people really do, not what the QMS states they do. Place them into the QMS.

8. Any time a value stream map is completed, update the process accordingly (in procedural or work instruction format) so that they are one and the same. I was pleasantly surprised one day after helping a client team complete a current value stream map, and I asked what should be done with it. The president spoke up and said that it should be transformed into the current procedure within the QMS. It was the answer I was looking for.

9. Add to the leader standard work of certain supervisors the need to review documents on a predetermined basis, for:

   a. Accuracy

   b. Viability

   c. Organization of the documents that are actually used

   d. Ease of users getting to these documents

   e. Storage of any uncontrolled documents

   This review should be performed in conjunction with reviewing how well process improvements made during kaizen events and other improvement activities have been sustained.

K. STANDARDIZING THE QMS DOCUMENTATION

In the business environment, whatever has been done in an area or for a process through the first three S's, the objective would now be to standardize it throughout the entire facility. If a green box painted on the floor with a two-inch-wide paint brush is used to signify incoming product, then the following items would be standardized throughout the building:

Green = Incoming product location

Painted lines are two inches wide

The green color would be specified with a Pantone color number

In the world of QMS documentation, standardization would primarily be focused on procedure format, work instruction format, and file name format.

It is important to clearly define the difference between a procedure and a work instruction, perhaps in the Document Control procedure or better yet, on templates that are used by employees.

The typical definition of a documented procedure is that it is a document that tells *who* does *what, when,* and *where.* A work instruction defines *how* one of the procedural steps is actually done. (One company I worked with had already defined these terms on their own before I came to assist. They defined a work instruction as "Tells who and how work is performed." The "who" is incorrect and is one reason why employees were confused about the distinction between the two documents and why their documentation system grew so much.)

Even after defining these terms correctly, people still get confused identifying what is actually a procedure and what is actually a work instruction. Some documents start off as work instructions and then wander off into becoming procedures. Much of this results from employees, who are now authors, not knowing the difference between the two types of documents because there is nothing in the system to train them or inform them on the difference.

So in addition to the above definitions, I further define a procedure as a "Document that states actions performed by multiple people or multiple departments." I also further define a work instruction as a "Document that describes the steps performed by one person or one department." These two additional definitions seem to make understanding the difference between a procedure and a work instruction more clear to people.

L. LEAN PROCEDURE AND WORK INSTRUCTION FORMAT

Most companies have made attempts to standardize on document formats, and then entropy reared its ugly head again as the formats began to become anything but standardized. This is nothing new to the reader. However, what is new is now that we have sorted out the wasteful and redundant sections, we will determine the format that is least wasteful, which will now be standardized throughout the facility.

For a procedure, it's recommended to only include the Purpose, Scope, Procedure (which consists of Responsibility and Action), and Revision Record.

1. *Purpose.* This section should explain *why* the procedure exists. Most authors write *what* the procedure *contains*, such as in this example of a purpose statement for an internal audit procedure: "The purpose of this procedure is to define the responsibilities and requirements for planning and conducting audits, in addition to reporting audit results and maintenance of the records." This explains "what" is in the procedure, not "why" the procedure exists. A better purpose statement would be: "The purpose of this procedure is to assess the degree to which our internal processes conform to ISO 9001 and our QMS as well as assess the effectiveness of these processes in meeting our process objectives. The assessments are used as a means of driving continual improvement of the effectiveness of our QMS."

2. *Scope.* This section is often misunderstood, as is evidenced by the following example from a real company in which the same scope statement was written in every procedure: "This procedure applies to all operations in the ABC Company." Remember, if a statement is repeated more than once, it is not adding value. This statement, written in every procedure that the organization had, did not add value.

The key words in the Scope section are "applies to." One should list every product, service, department, facility (if more than one), or document this procedure applies to. If necessary to make a clear distinction, I have occasionally referred to what the procedure does not apply to, as in this example of a document control procedure: "This procedure applies to the control of quality manual, procedures, work instructions, and forms, both electronic and in hard copy form, for all three sites. It does not apply to the control of drawings or external documents."

3. *Procedure.* I recommend dividing this section into two sections (columns) as shown in Figure 2.5. The first section (column) is the "Responsibility" section, which forces the writer to identify "who" is responsible for each paragraph.

The second section (column) is the action that occurs. This section should always start with a verb or a participle phrase (that is, an "if" or "when" phrase followed by a verb).

4. *Revision Record.* This section should include "what" changed in the procedure, the new revision level or date, and the approvals, much like a part drawing has a revision history. It is not necessary to maintain a list of every change that has ever been made in the "Revision Record" section, especially if the organization is archiving the previous documents anyway.

3.1 Responsibility	3.2 Action
Any employee	1. Initiates the change or addition of a document (quality manual section, procedure, work instruction, or form) by submitting a draft or marked-up copy to the management representative using the existing format of comparable documents.
Management representative	2. Reviews the document for initial approval and advises the employee of changes to be made. Reviews the document to ensure: • Compatibility with ISO 9001:2000 • Compatibility with customer and internal requirements • No redundancy with current documentation • That the change/addition/deletion adds value to the system • Analysis of possible elimination of other documentation (that is, words, sentences, paragraphs, or entire documents) If acceptable, initiates the process of changing and/or adding to the document.

Figure 2.5 A good example of a procedure format.

An organization may decide to keep the information from just the most recent revision.

Characteristics of a Well-Written Procedure

A procedure should explain "who" does "what" and, if applicable, "when" and "where." The format recommended above forces the "who" to be defined, which is oftentimes lacking in many company procedures.

The following recommendations will allow for an efficient, effective, nonredundant and useful procedure.

1. Although there may be a few exceptions, most procedures should not exceed three pages. The actual procedure should start on the first page, not on the second, third, or fourth page as in the example shown in Figure 2.3.

2. There should never be any redundancy of statements made within a procedure or between procedures and/or work instructions.

3. Procedures should refer to other documents or forms (by actual title and number, if applicable) within the body of the procedure at the point in the process in which they would be used.

4. Avoid describing how to fill out a form (that is, "Where it states 'date,' record today's date"). Just state, "fill out the form completely" or "complete section I of the form."

5. Make your forms self-explanatory and, if necessary, insert examples on the form itself since this is what people are actually completing. An example of this for a corrective action form might be: "Verification (that is, review documents and training records and visually verify that the action is working)."

6. Procedures shouldn't have forms attached to them. Forms are stand-alone documents.

7. Procedures should contain electronic linkages to other documents so that, if necessary, the user is only a click away from reading them.

For a work instruction, it is recommended to include just two sections: "Action" and "Revision Record." A work instruction should only describe *how* a procedural step is performed, by one job title (for example, inspector, engineer, customer service representative) or one department (for example, Production).

Action. Start with a verb. There's no need to state responsibility since it was already stated in the procedure referring to the work instruction. If one is trying to write a work instruction and there are different people responsible for different tasks, then this document, or a portion of it, should be in a procedure.

Revision record. Same as a procedure.

Who Approves the Document?

When referring to ISO 9001, we oftentimes use the words "process owner." When referring to lean, we oftentimes use the words "value stream manager." They are essentially the same person with two different titles that mean the same thing. One way or the other, if this person truly owns the process, he or she should only be approving the document along with the management representative. The purpose for each approval (that is, management representative, process owner) should be defined as was done in Figure 2.5 above.

Miscellaneous Notes About Standardization of QMS Documents

1. Another way to ensure a standardized format is to purchase a document control software program. The author, however, has found these to often be bottlenecks and recommends maximizing the capabilities of all Microsoft Office products, including Word, Excel, Visio, Access, Outlook, and SharePoint.

2. Also, the above recommendations assume the reader has *not* ventured into the use of lean documents such as *combination work sheets* (CWS) and/or *job breakdown sheets* (JBS) as part of the TWI Job Instruction module. If the reader's company has done so, the recommended format for a work instruction would change, as its features would most likely be combined with the features of a CWS and/or JBS. In other words, we would not want to add documents that cover some of the same material that already exists in other documents without trying to combine them and eliminate more redundancy.

3. File names should also be standardized and easy to read. As mentioned earlier, they should not begin alphanumerically with letters and numbers that mean nothing to most people. They should start with a key word that means something to the reader so that when the reader searches for a file, it is easy to find because it is automatically sorted in alphabetic order.

4. Of course, one way to keep electronic files and folders standard is to limit the capabilities of users to make changes to the documents and to the organization of those documents.

5. If hard copies of documents exist in binders, it is wise to standardize on their organization and perhaps even use colored tabs that have some defined meaning protruding from the first page of the document for ease of finding a searched-for document.

6. Oftentimes, it is wise to standardize what is located on employees' computer desktops. In one company, this was done for five order entry personnel because the team leader would oftentimes provide training or assistance at each person's desk in their cubicle. The training was more consistent and efficient with standardized desktop icons.

M. SUSTAINING A LEAN QMS

Arguably the most difficult part of any lean or 5S effort is sustaining the gains. This is due, once again, to the effects of entropy. Everything proceeds in the direction of disorder, including QMS documentation.

One reason for this is because no one has ever really made an attempt to control the size of the documents. Many management representatives are happy to get new documents from other employees because it seems like that means they are actually using the system and contributing to it.

It is imperative to be aware now that lean and quality need to be heading in the same direction. Both lean and quality, whether represented by departments, individuals, philosophies, or practices, need to be thinking in terms of getting rid of process wastes, as reflected in the real world and in process documents (that is, procedures, work instructions).

In Figure 2.5, the approval role of the management representative is defined. Describing the management representative's document approval role in this way will help to sustain the document organization.

When I 5S'd my closet, I got rid of 161 pieces of clothing. I also moved six of my suits from a downstairs closet (warehouse) to my bedroom closet and eliminated the bin in the garage that contained winter clothes in the summer and summer clothes in the winter because I now had so much space. I was concerned that I would not be able to sustain my improvements. I made a vow to myself, and hung up a sign in my closet as a reminder, that anytime I received a new shirt or new pants for my birthday or Christmas, I would get rid of another one of the same type. Why can't this same vow be made with QMS documentation? Any time a new document is added, there has to be a check to see if another document can be removed that basically covers the same topic. At the very least, an attempt must be made!

Many companies "sustain" their 5S improvements via a regularly scheduled 5S assessment, using a checklist of questions, and the posting of the results. This can also be done on the QMS documentation system. It is best, once the *sort, set in order, shine,* and *standardize* steps are complete, to take photos and screen shots of the way things should be and use this as a comparative tool during the assessment performed during the *sustain* step of 5S.

Completing this assessment and posting the results should be part of a leader's standard work to ensure ongoing completion and sustainability.

3

Integrating Lean Practices with the QMS

A. WORK INSTRUCTIONS ADDRESSING LEAN PRACTICES

The leaders of your organization must ask themselves this very important question: "Are lean principles, culture, processes, and tools going to be a part of our organization permanently or are they going to go away sometime in the near future?" If the answer to this question is that lean will be part of the organization permanently, then make it a permanent part of the QMS.

If you foresee that value stream mapping will be a process that will be performed continually, take the words from your training material and develop a work instruction out of them, as is shown in Figure 3.1. In this way, the value stream mapping work instruction becomes your company's process, and it is now more easily improved based on your experiences. The work instruction in Figure 3.1 was adapted from material in Mike Rother and John Shook's book *Learning to See.*

Of course, as stated in the previous chapter, we can not just add a work instruction without another document referring to it. Perhaps the best possible procedures within your system that might initiate a value stream mapping process would be:

- Management review

- Quality planning, and/or

- Corrective/preventive actions

	Title: Value Stream Mapping	
	Doc. No: QAW-Q06	**Revision:** 0
		Page: 1 of 3

Instructions:

1. Determine and identify a value stream manager based on the requirements of the Job Description (JD-35).

2. Assemble a multidisciplinary team that includes those employees who are actually involved in the process.

3. Determine and identify product family by completing a Selection Form (QAF-64)

   3.1 Obtain customer information and delivery schedule.

   3.2 Ensure that the product family members share at least 75% of the same processes.

   3.3 Compute "takt time" by dividing the total amount of seconds available per day (Work time—Breaks) by the average daily total demand for the identified product family.

4. Develop current Value Stream Map

   4.1 Obtain a long piece of paper and hang on the wall.

   4.2 Define your beginning and end points.

   4.3 Perform quick walk-through to identify main processes (in sequence).

   4.4 Have one person draw a "spaghetti chart," completing the path and distance on a plant layout, during the walk-through

   4.5 Map the entire process, step by step, starting with the first step (that is, Enter Order), by recording an action word (verb) first, and using no more than three words. Record each of these steps on a specific color sticky note (that is, yellow) and place in sequential order from left to right with pencil-drawn connectors.

      4.5.1 In between each step, identify and record any "Queue Times" on a specific color sticky note (that is, blue) and place on the paper below the main value stream map between the two process steps.

      4.5.2 In between each step, identify and record any "Inventory" amounts in terms of days of inventory on a specific color sticky note (that is, pink) by drawing a triangle with an "I" and place on the paper below the main value stream map between the two process steps. The inventory days are calculated by determining an average number of pieces/subs/WIP/FG in that area divided by the calculated "takt" time.

Figure 3.1   Value stream mapping work instruction example.

	Title: Value Stream Mapping	
	Doc. No: QAW-Q06	**Revision:** 0
		Page: 2 of 3

4.5.3 Record the Raw Material coming into the process and the average amount of inventory for each Raw Material on the same colored sticky note (that is, yellow) as the main steps, and connect to the Main Value Stream.

4.5.4 Beneath each step, obtain and record the average data required to define each step's performance attributes on a Manufacturing Data Box (QAF-65), and place beneath each major step, including:

4.5.4.1 Cycle Time—on a per piece basis.

4.5.5 Record Actions on an Action List displayed for all to see; set responsibilities and due dates.

4.6 Beneath the Value Stream Map, record the Value-Added Time (Production Lead Time) and Non-Value-Added Time (Overall Processing Time) on a two-tiered horizontal line, with the Production Lead Time on the top line.

4.7 Add up the total amounts, record the totals, and compute the percentage of Value-Added Time.

4.8 Identify each step's contribution to value with a colored dot sticker, such as:

4.8.1 Red: Non-Value-Added steps

4.8.2 Blue: Non-Value-Added steps, but necessary today

4.8.3 Green: Value-Added steps

4.9 Identify Opportunities for Improvement, some of which will be Kaizen Events, and record them on a specific colored sticky note (that is, green) and place on the Value Stream Map.

5. Develop Future State Map

5.1 Ensure it is known that the Future State is how we would like to see the process in 12 months.

5.2 Decide what Kaizen Events will be initiated and completed within the year and assume that these will be done when drawing the Future State Map.

5.3 Repeat step 4.5 for the Future State.

5.4 Critique Opportunities for Improvement and record those actions on the VSM Kaizen Event To Do List (QAF-66) that can be accomplished within the next year.

Figure 3.1 *Continued.*

	Title: Value Stream Mapping	
	Doc. No: QAW-Q06	Revision: 0
		Page: 3 of 3

5.5   After prioritizing and selecting Kaizen Events, initiate the Kaizen Events Procedure (QAP-Q05).

5.6   Estimate inventory and time savings and record them on the bottom of the Current Value Stream and as an Impact on the To Do List.

5.7   Calculate improvement in Overall Processing Time and reduction in inventory, after suggested improvements.

Revision Record			
Rev.	Date	Approval	Description of revision
0	09-20-xx	M. Micklewright	Initial release

Figure 3.1   *Continued.*

Perhaps your organization's leadership wants the 5S process to exist permanently. How about a work instruction on how to do 5S? The work instruction in Figure 3.2 was summarized from information obtained from the Productivity Press Development Team's book *5S for Operators.*

As in the last example, we can not just add a work instruction without another document referring to it. Perhaps the best possible procedures within your system that might initiate a 5S process and should refer to this new work instruction might be:

- Process control

- Quality planning

- Internal auditing, and/or

- Corrective/preventive actions

For another example of a lean process, value stream mapping, written as a work instruction, refer to Figure 3.1 on page 88.

Other Documents Addressing Lean Practices

Some companies have new lean titles including:

Kaizen Team Leader

Lean Champion

Sensei

Value Stream Manager

5S Assessor

Whether these positions are permanent or part-time, it is suggested to put them in the same job description format—assuming they are controlled—as your company has them documented in its current quality management system. I make the same suggestion for internal auditors and lead auditors in any QMS. There is no need to develop a new lean format or structure for lean documents. This would be wasteful.

Any lean forms (for example, standard work combination sheets, 5S evaluation forms, job breakdown sheets, and leader standard work) should also be treated just like any form in the quality management system. By doing this, one might find out if there are duplicate or nearly duplicate documents. In one case, the president of an ISO/TS 16949–certified

Title: 5S	
Doc. no.: QAW-	Revision: 0
Date: July, 2006	Page: 1 of 6

Printed copies are for reference only. Shred immediately after use.

1.0   *Purpose.* The purpose of this work instruction is to define the process of conducting a 5S (*sort, set in order, shine, standardize, sustain*) event in support of lean manufacturing processes and maintaining a neat and clean factory that leads to:

1) Higher productivity

2) Fewer defects

3) Meeting deadlines better

4) A much safer place to work

2.0   *Instructions:*

   2.1   *Sort*

      2.1.1   Launch the red-tag project by:

         2.1.1.1   Organizing the team, supplies, a time or schedule to perform red-tagging,

         2.1.1.2   Setting aside a local red-tag holding area, and

         2.1.1.3   Planning for disposal of red-tagged items

      2.1.2   Identify red-tag targets such as:

         2.1.2.1   The specific types of items to evaluate

         2.1.2.2   The physical areas where red-tagging will take place

      2.1.3   Set red-tag criteria:

         2.1.3.1   Example: Items needed for the next month are kept in a specific location; items that are not needed can be disposed of or stored in a separate location

         2.1.3.2   Example: The quantity of the item needed to perform this work in the next month

      2.1.4   Make (or buy) red tags

      2.1.5   Attach the red tags quickly. Do the whole target area (or factory) in 1–2 days

      2.1.6   Evaluate the red-tagged Items

      2.1.7   Log and track the results of red-tagging

Figure 3.2   5S work instruction example.
Source: Productivity Press Development Team, *5S for Operators* (New York: Productivity Press, 1996).

Title: 5S	
Doc. no.: QAW-	Revision: 0
Date: July, 2006	Page: 2 of 6

2.2   *Set in order*

    2.2.1   Decide on appropriate locations

        2.2.1.1   Locate items by frequency of use

        2.2.1.2   Store items together if they are used together

        2.2.1.3   Store them in the sequence in which they are used

        2.2.1.4   Devise a "just let go" strategy

        2.2.1.5   Make storage areas larger than the items stored there for ease of retrieval

        2.2.1.6   Create few jigs, tools, and dies with multiple functions

        2.2.1.7   Store tools according to function or product

    2.2.2   Remove waste from human motion by following these principles:

        2.2.2.1   Start and end each motion with hands moving at once.

        2.2.2.2   Both arms should move symmetrically and in opposite directions

        2.2.2.3   Keep trunk motions to a minimum

        2.2.2.4   Use gravity instead of muscle

        2.2.2.5   Avoid zigzagging motions and sudden changes in direction

        2.2.2.6   Move with a steady rhythm

        2.2.2.7   Maintain a comfortable posture with comfortable motions

        2.2.2.8   Use the feet to operate on and off switches for machines where practical

        2.2.2.9   Keep materials and tools close and in front

        2.2.2.10   Arrange materials and tools close and in front

        2.2.2.11   Use inexpensive methods for feeding in and sending out materials

        2.2.2.12   Stand at a proper height for the work to be done

        2.2.2.13   Make materials and parts easy to pick up

Figure 3.2   *Continued.*

Title: 5S	
Doc. no.: QAW-	**Revision:** 0
Date: July, 2006	**Page:** 3 of 6

2.2.2.14 Make handles and grips in efficient, easy-to-use shapes and positions

2.2.3 Create a 5S map to evaluate current locations of parts, jigs, tools, dies, equipment, and machinery to decide best locations, as follows:

2.2.3.1 Make a floor plan or area diagram identifying the location of everything within the work space to be studied

2.2.3.2 Draw arrows on the plan showing the work flow between items in the work space. Number them in the order they occur, one arrow for each operation

2.2.3.3 Review and identify areas of congestion and potential waste elimination

2.2.3.4 Make a new 5S layout for the work space

2.2.3.5 Analyze the efficiency of this layout

2.2.3.6 Continue to experiment with other possible layouts

2.2.3.7 Implement the new layout

2.2.3.8 Continue to evaluate and improve

2.2.4 Identify locations so that everyone will now know what goes where and how many of each belong in each location by using:

2.2.4.1 The *signboard* strategy (location, item, and quantity indicators)

2.2.4.2 The *painting* strategy, using standardized colors for

2.2.4.2.1 Floors and walkways

2.2.4.2.2 Cart storage locations

2.2.4.2.3 Aisle direction

2.2.4.2.4 Door opening range

2.2.4.2.5 Work tables

2.2.4.2.6 Tiger marks, to show where inventory and equipment should not be placed, or to show hazardous areas

Figure 3.2 *Continued.*

Title: 5S	
Doc. no.: QAW-	**Revision:** 0
Date: July, 2006	**Page:** 4 of 6

            2.2.4.3   The "after" 5S map

            2.2.4.4   The *color coding* strategy (to identify purpose of tools, and so on)

            2.2.4.5   The *outlining* strategy

   2.3   *Shine*

        2.3.1   Determine the cleaning/inspecting targets including warehouse items, equipment, and space

        2.3.2   Determine cleaning/inspecting assignments by marking and posting them on:

            2.3.2.1   A 5S assignment map

            2.3.2.2   A 5S schedule of days and times

        2.3.3   Determine cleaning/inspecting methods and create a checklist by:

            2.3.3.1   Determining what will be cleaned/inspected in each area and what supplies and equipment will be used

            2.3.3.2   Performing the *five-minute shine*

            2.3.3.3   Creating standards for cleaning/inspecting procedures

        2.3.4   Prepare cleaning/inspecting tools and store them where they are easy to find, use, and return

        2.3.5   Start to *shine* and use all of your senses to detect abnormalities:

            2.3.5.1   Watch for slight defects (such as oil leakage, wear, warping, color changes)

            2.3.5.2   Listen for changes in sounds

            2.3.5.3   Smell unusual odors or burning smells

            2.3.5.4   Touch the machine to detect deviations from normal (for example, wear, wobbling)

        2.3.6   Correct equipment problems instantly or request maintenance and log onto a checklist of needed maintenance activities

   2.4   *Standardize*

        2.4.1   Assign 3S (sort, set in order, shine) Responsibilities by using 5S maps, 5S schedules, or job cycle charts

Figure 3.2 *Continued.*

Title: 5S	
Doc. no.: QAW-	**Revision:** 0
Date: July, 2006	**Page:** 5 of 6

    2.4.2   Integrate 3S duties into regular work duties through:

        2.4.2.1   Visual 5S

        2.4.2.2   Five-minute 5S so that work is brief, efficient, and habitual. Signboards may help

    2.4.3   Check on the 3S maintenance level by using a standardization-level checklist and completing to a schedule (for example, weekly)

    2.4.4   Find ways to *prevent:*

        2.4.4.1   Unneeded Items from accumulating

        2.4.4.2   Things from having to be put back by making it difficult or impossible to put things in the wrong place via:

            2.4.4.2.1   Suspension

            2.4.4.2.2   *Incorporation,* in which jigs, tools, and measuring devices are smoothly integrated into the process or devices are stored where they are used and do not have to be returned

            2.4.4.2.3   Use *elimination* via:

                2.4.4.2.3.1   Tool unification (combining functions into one tool)

                2.4.4.2.3.2   Tool substitution (replacing the tool's function with something else)

                2.4.4.2.3.3   Method substitution

        2.4.4.3   Things from getting dirty

  2.5   *Sustain*

    2.5.1   Create conditions or a structure that will help sustain a commitment to the five pillars. These might include:

        2.5.1.1   Awareness

        2.5.1.2   Time

        2.5.1.3   Structure

Figure 3.2   *Continued.*

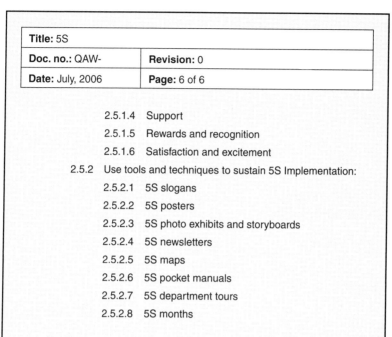

Title: 5S	
Doc. no.: QAW-	**Revision:** 0
Date: July, 2006	**Page:** 6 of 6

        2.5.1.4 Support

        2.5.1.5 Rewards and recognition

        2.5.1.6 Satisfaction and excitement

    2.5.2 Use tools and techniques to sustain 5S Implementation:

        2.5.2.1 5S slogans

        2.5.2.2 5S posters

        2.5.2.3 5S photo exhibits and storyboards

        2.5.2.4 5S newsletters

        2.5.2.5 5S maps

        2.5.2.6 5S pocket manuals

        2.5.2.7 5S department tours

        2.5.2.8 5S months

Revision Record			
Rev.	Date	By	Description of revision
0	09/20/05	M. Micklewright	Initial release

Approvals		
Title	Signature	Date
QA Manager	R. Infusino	10/25/05

Figure 3.2 *Continued.*

organization asked me what I thought of his new Waste Walk form (see Figure 3.3).

I told him his form was wasteful because it basically contained the same elements as his Corrective/Preventive Action form. Perhaps, if the two forms—one from "quality" and one from "lean"—had been colocated, more people would have seen the waste.

B. AUDITING FOR LEAN AND GEMBA WALKS

A training coordinator for a custom packaging company was interested in furthering the skills of the company's internal auditors and improving the audit program. I had proposed a class in "Auditing for Lean" and provided her with the agenda. She said she would take the proposal to the ISO Steering Team to see what they all thought. Soon after, she e-mailed me:

> Hi Mike,
>
> I did bring it up at the Steering Team and they were a bit concerned that the training may be more of a distraction for our auditors than a help . . . I don't want to make lean people out of auditors.

What a shame, I thought. Once again, this comment provides evidence of the division of responsibility between quality and lean people. Rather than seeing all forms of improvement (quality and lean) completely and totally linked to each other, the Steering Team sees "quality" responsibilities and "lean" responsibilities as being separate and distinct. The Steering Team did not "want to make lean people out of auditors" or distract the auditors with thoughts of observing waste, even though auditors are supposed to be auditing for effectiveness.

Auditors Need to Know About Waste!

ISO 9001 requires that auditors audit for 1) compliance and 2) effectiveness. The first part is easy. Most auditors are trained to audit for compliance to the standard of interest and the company's procedures. Most audit programs do little in the way of auditing for effectiveness. This is why so many employees view the audit process so negatively and feel that it is a policing activity. The prevailing thought is that "they (the auditors) are only trying to catch me doing something that goes against the written word. Even though they say they are not auditing me, it sure feels like it. Even

Waste Elimination/Process Action Form

During waste walk	Department:	
	Performance area affected ❏ Safety ❏ Quality ❏ Costs ❏ Delivery	
	Type of waste ❏ Transportation ❏ Inventory ❏ Motion ❏ Waiting ❏ Overproduction ❏ Overprocessing ❏ Defects	
	Waste description:	
	Details:	
	Date:	
	Identified by:	
After waste walk	**Why?** (Why is wasteful activity happening?)	
	What? (What can be done to eliminate or reduce the detected waste?)	Immediate
		Permanent
	Who? (Who is responsible for action?)	Immediate
		Permanent
	When? (When will it be done?)	Immediate
		Permanent
	Action results	Immediate
		Permanent
After action review	**Waste eliminated?**	❏ Removed ❏ Reduced ❏ Still there
	If no . . . action needed	

Figure 3.3 Waste walk form.

though they say they are trying to help improve the system, they are not. They are just trying to catch us."

This is where internal audit programs can learn from the principles behind doing gemba walks, which will be discussed in more detail in a forthcoming section.

For now it is just important to understand that, no matter what you call it, having process waste is not effective. If an auditor is observing process waste and writing up a preventive action based on her observation, she is "auditing for effectiveness," which is what she should be doing whether one calls it "lean" or not.

The eight commonly accepted process wastes are as follows:

1. Defects

2. Overproduction

3. Waiting

4. Not using employees' minds or skills

5. Transportation

6. Inventory

7. Motion

8. Excess processing

When an auditor (or for that matter, any employee) observes the first process waste on the list, "defects," it is commonly understood and accepted that he should record a corrective action so that the root cause can be determined and a good corrective action can be put into place. If auditors are not aware of the negative effects of waste on the quality management system, they may be encouraging more paperwork, more work instructions, and more steps to follow in the corrective actions performed by other employees within the organization.

The next seven process wastes after "defects" lead to ineffectiveness, which is what auditors are supposed to be auditing for. They should know about these wastes and how to "see" them, which is what the gemba walk teaches employees. Upon seeing waste, auditors can write up preventive actions, which should initiate an improvement or kaizen event.

But Who Audits the Audit Program to Determine If It Is Effective?

No one audits the audit program for effectiveness, for the most part—not even your registrar auditor.

We must also realize and face up to the fact that many audit programs themselves are very ineffective. We must find out why internal audit programs are ineffective because the reasons can be roadblocks to any desire to improve an internal audit system. It would be proper for a company to do a root cause analysis on why its audit program is so ineffective. I challenge the reader to do this for your own internal audit program. Here are some possible reasons your internal audit program may be ineffective:

1. Registrar auditors are too easy themselves because their desire is to maintain your business and not tick you off with probation or too many nonconformities. If the registrar auditors are easy, then the internal auditors will oftentimes follow suit and be easy as well. The definition of "easy" in this case is an auditor who may witness many nonconformities, and even point them out throughout the audit day, but then only write up one or two of them.

2. Registrar auditors, especially those who are part-time consultants, are too easy because they want to maintain your business and ensure job security for themselves.

3. Top management truly does not understand the spirit of ISO 9001 and ISO 9004, and the spirit behind an internal audit system.

4. ISO 9001 still uses the word "quality" in its title and therefore it is perceived as a thing only "quality" people do, definitely not what "lean" people do.

5. Top management jumps to the next craze (such as Six Sigma, lean, balanced scorecard, reengineering) without understanding that they are really just subsets of a QMS—a QMS that contains an internal audit program that could support these crazes and the improvements that may come as a result of using them.

6. Top management wants to believe that if the registrar finds few nonconformities, they must be pretty good and don't really need to improve any processes, including internal auditing.

7. We act as bad children and the auditors act as bad parents. Just like when Mom and Dad tell their children to clean up their room and they do so by throwing their stuff under the bed. The auditor stops by, sees the stuff under the bed, and ignores it as if it is not there. The audit program, at all levels, becomes a joke and there's no need to improve it.

8. Internal auditors are:

- Taught to how to audit for compliance, not for effectiveness

- Trained only once

- Not given feedback on their performance

- Not supported properly by top management

- Not acting as investigators by obtaining their own samples and collecting evidence

- Not rejecting poor corrective action responses resulting from "operator error"–type "root" causes

9. Though required, the internal audit process itself is not evaluated internally for effectiveness.

10. Internal audits are viewed as a necessary evil and are only performed to comply with the standard. Why improve them?

11. "The registrar auditor did not write me up for it, how can an internal auditor?"

12. Some internal audit programs allow for wimpy observations in which a nonconformity, wasteful action, or potential nonconformity is written up as an observation, but no action is required, so no action is completed.

13. Internal audits are conducted in batches, or continually, sometimes once a year or once a month. In contrast, a gemba walk is done more continuously. Therefore, internal audits are not a way of life, but rather an interruption of life.

14. Internal auditors use CAPA (corrective action/preventive action) forms; leaners use waste walk forms or some other lean form, as previously discussed.

15. Auditing is only about auditing against procedures; it's not really about improving the effectiveness of the systems in place.

16. No one wants to do audits; kaizen events are where it's at.

Whatever the root causes are to the ineffectiveness of a company's internal audit program, it is wise to go through the root cause analysis process and rectify the issues before just blindly accepting and acting on what is written in this chapter.

Tools and patches do not work without first eliminating the root causes of problems.

Auditor Qualifications

ISO 19011, *Guidelines for quality and/or environmental management systems auditing,* suggests that ideal auditors should have the following characteristics:

- Ethical
- Open-minded
- Diplomatic
- Observant
- Perceptive
- Versatile
- Tenacious
- Decisive
- Self-reliant

One could argue that these are many of the same characteristics that should be possessed by a "true leader." A true leader is the type of person who should be conducting gemba walks. The skills of an internal auditor should be married with the skills of a leader who performs gemba walks to increase the value of each process. But what is a gemba walk?

How the Gemba Walk Relates to Internal Auditing

Gemba is the more popular term of the original phrase *genchi genbutsu.* Gemba means "the actual place." Genchi genbutsu means "going to the place to see the actual situation for understanding."

Internal auditors should be "going to the place to see the actual situation for understanding." Auditors should be doing genchi genbutsu, or the *gemba walk,* and if they are not, they are doing what the auditors of yesteryear used to do—auditing in the conference room.

Now that we understand that auditors should be doing the gemba walk and that they should possess the same characteristics as gemba walkers, it is necessary to discuss the other characteristics of the gemba walk. Some of the characteristics and skills of a gemba walker that should be qualities of any internal auditor are listed below.

Characteristics and skills of a gemba walker that can be applied to an internal auditor:

1. *Seeing waste. An internal auditor can learn the skill of "seeing waste" after thorough training and coaching and going on gemba walks with experienced waste seers. Internal auditors need to understand the eight process wastes and be able to see any type of waste, whether process or otherwise.*

2. Following the process. Some internal auditors have this skill set already. Many more think they know how to follow a process, but don't. They are still too wrapped up in auditing for compliance, not effectiveness, or they still don't know how to do a process audit. See Figure 3.4.

3. *Gemba walkers (GWs) are coaches. This may sound contradictory to what an auditor should be, but it is not. When on the gemba walk, a GW asks questions of the person working in an area. The GW may question how things are done (like an auditor does) and point out the wastes in the process. A GW will not provide answers (like an auditor should not), yet will question the person working in the area (the auditee) on how the process could be done differently or the area set up differently to rid the process of waste.*

4. *A gemba walker:*

   • Teaches by stretching the worker's thinking about their perceptions

   • Challenges the worker to consider entirely new possibilities

   • Points out wastes, noncritically

   • Asks how a process can be done differently and more easily for the worker's benefit

5. Gemba walking is usually performed on a regularly set schedule, like an audit *but much more frequently (that is, weekly rather than semiannually).*

6. GWs follow up on assigned actions (like an auditor).

7. Seeing results from gemba walking requires patience and tolerance (like auditing). It is not fast. Six months of weekly gemba walks is the low end of the time frame that is necessary to develop the benefits of true mentoring and leading.

8. *Gemba walking requires lean management as a mind-set.*

9. *GWs should include all levels of management, including the CEO.*

10. *GWs should look for:*

    • *Production tracking charts updated throughout the day*

    • *Recorded reasons for misses (that is, not achieving the production goal for that hour)*

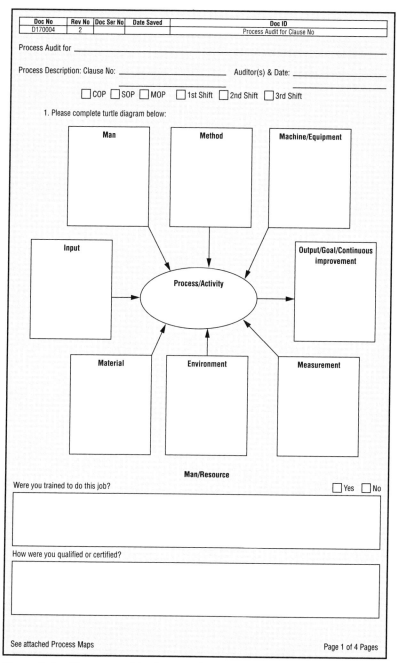

Figure 3.4 "Process auditing" at a real company? This form *is not* conducive to process auditing.

Doc No	Rev No	Doc Ser No	Date Saved	Doc ID
D170004	2			Process Audit for Clause No

Process Audit for _____

Process Description: Clause No: _____   Auditor(s) & Date: _____

☐ COP ☐ SOP ☐ MOP   ☐ 1st Shift ☐ 2nd Shift ☐ 3rd Shift

Have you had any ongoing training or need any training to perform the job more efficiently?   ☐ Yes ☐ No

Machinery
Are the proper machines being used for this process?   ☐ Yes ☐ No

How are they maintained?

Materials
Are the proper materials being used for this process?   ☐ Yes ☐ No

Do the materials meet process/product specifications?   ☐ Yes ☐ No

Methods
How do you know what to do? Do you have access to procedures, flowcharts, work instructions, and such? Show me.

Who does what, when, and how? Describe.

See attached Process Maps   Page 2 of 4 Pages

Figure 3.4 *Continued.*

Doc No	Rev No	Doc Ser No	Date Saved	Doc ID
D170004	2			Process Audit for Clause No

Process Audit for _____

Process Description: Clause No: _____ Auditor(s) & Date: _____

☐ COP ☐ SOP ☐ MOP ☐ 1st Shift ☐ 2nd Shift ☐ 3rd Shift

Measures

Are measurement outputs utilized to continuously improve the process? ☐ Yes ☐ No

Do you check the output? How and what do you check it against? ☐ Yes ☐ No

What forms are being used to record findings?

Flowchart

Is the flowchart an accurate representation of the process? Indicate discrepancies. ☐ Yes ☐ No

Environment

Is this environment suitable for the operating process? ☐ Yes ☐ No

Are there any workstation requirements (safety, ergonomics) for performing this job? ☐ Yes ☐ No

Process

Have the inputs been converted to the desired outputs? ☐ Yes ☐ No

See attached Process Maps   Page 3 of 4 Pages

Figure 3.4 *Continued.*

Doc No	Rev No	Doc Ser No	Date Saved	Doc ID
D170004	2			Process Audit for Clause No

Process Audit for _____

Process Description: Clause No: _____ Auditor(s) & Date: _____

☐ COP ☐ SOP ☐ MOP   ☐ 1st Shift ☐ 2nd Shift ☐ 3rd Shift

Results

☐ Conforms   ☐ Minor nonconformity   ☐ Major nonconformity

Findings/Opportunities for improvement:

Strengths:

See attached Process Maps   Page 4 of 4 Pages

Figure 3.4   *Continued.*

- *Visually displayed action lists with due dates and responsibilities*
- *Proof of daily communication of results and actions*
- *Workplace organization, perhaps including:*
  - *Weekly 5S audit form*
  - *Visible and current cleaning routines and checklists*
  - *Current maintenance checklists*
  - *Clearly visible indicators of location and quantity for each object in the area*
  - *Reorder points for material and a displayed process for reordering*
  - *Correct kanban quantities in use*

Assuming that it is agreed that auditors should be practicing genchi genbutsu *(going to the place to see the actual situation for understanding)*—and I do not know why they would not be—auditors, management representatives, and audit coordinators could expand the usefulness and the effectiveness of the internal audit program by learning and adopting the characteristics listed above that they currently do not possess. I have *italicized* those characteristics above that most internal auditors currently do *not* possess. Top management should lead this effort because it is top management that is responsible for the effectiveness of the organization as a whole.

If top management is truly committed to the ideals of ISO 9001 and lean, it should be striving to look for ways of improving both. The melding of internal audit practices with gemba walking is one way of improving both and eliminating any redundancies.

In doing so, an organization must ask itself some of the following questions:

1. In the spirit of always studying and being at the process, should audits be done more frequently, like a gemba walk, rather than less frequently, like a typical quarterly or annual audit? See "Layered Process Audits and Their Relationship to Gemba Walking" below.

2. Should the two processes be melded into one process? What would it be called? Internal auditing (with gemba attributes)? Gemba walking (with internal auditing attributes)? Gemba auditing? Something else?

3. If it is still called internal auditing (with gemba attributes), should preventive actions be generated when waste is witnessed? This will be discussed more in the next section.

4. Should some of our top managers participate more in the audit/gemba process?

5. Should our auditors receive leadership or coaching training?

6. Should our lean and quality departments be one department?

A onetime client of mine asked me to teach their auditors a refresher class in internal auditing. As usual, I taught the theoretical aspects of auditing and the ISO 9001 standard from an auditor's perspective first and then I customized the class to use their internal audit procedure and forms. I also walked them through a short but real-life audit of one of their processes using their forms, and so on. Several years prior to this class, at the suggestion of their registrar auditor, the company had changed their audit checklist form from one that was more element-based to one that was more in line with doing a "process audit," or so they thought. They thought, and they were instructed, that if they completed a turtle diagram first by regrouping and batching information into categories (man, method, machine, measurement, material, environment) from what was a process-oriented procedure, and then asked two or three standard questions from the standard checklist shown in Figure 3.4, page 105, they were doing a "process" audit. They were so misled by their auditor. Performing an audit using this checklist was not a process audit because they were not following the process! Recording information into batches or categories when actually conducting the audit was serving no purpose at all. They admitted that it served no purpose, but this is what they thought they had to do. I then showed them how to do a process audit, and they loved it. They thought it was so much easier and made so much more sense. The company eventually got rid of the form and developed a checklist to be used so that specific questions pertaining to the process of interest would be recorded. They then started to actually follow the process while auditing.

What Does ISO 9004:2000 State?*

If one believes, as I do, that ISO 9004 *(Quality management systems—Guidelines for performance improvements)* represents the spirit behind

---

* At the time of this writing, ISO 9004:2009 had not been released in the U.S.

ISO 9001, then one should study it and learn how to improve their processes even more, including the internal audit process.

Section 8.2.1.3, Internal Audit, of ISO 9004 states that auditors should consider the following subjects for their internal audit process:

- Effective and efficient *implementation of processes*

- *Opportunities for continual improvement*

- *Capability of processes*

- Effective and efficient *use of statistical techniques*

- Use of information technology

- Analysis of quality cost data

- Effective and efficient *use of resources*

- *Process and product performance results and expectations*

- Adequacy and accuracy of performance measurement

- *Improvement activities*

- Relationships with interested parties

I have *italicized* the above subjects of consideration that could easily be considered "lean" matters, especially since in three cases the term "effective and efficient" is used.

This further goes to show that internal auditors should be learning about lean matters and should be hunting down and identifying waste that leads to "ineffective and inefficient" processes. This is not to say that auditors would become "lean" people, rather they would become better auditors.

Layered Process Audits and Their Relationship to Gemba Walking

The automotive industry has either strongly recommended or required its parts suppliers to perform what are called *layered process audits* (LPA). An LPA is an ongoing chain of simple verification checks, which, through observation, evaluations, and conversations on the production line, assure that the key work steps are being performed properly.[5] The focus in LPA is on checking items related to known problems and cause factors linked to high-risk problems. Most LPA checks look at inputs to the process (for example, equipment settings, conditions of tooling, craftsmanship, work sequence).

This is what might typically be written on a leader's standard work since one of the main responsibilities of a leader is to ensure that those who report to the leader are performing their standard work. An LPA fits in naturally with a lean culture, and since it is typically a very short process, it could easily be married to the gemba walk.

The attributes that an LPA shares with gemba walking, and not necessarily internal auditing, include:

1. They occur daily

2. They are performed by all layers of management, including the top layer, thus the term "layered"

3. Short time commitment

4. The focus is on the process, not the results

The possibility of highly improved effectiveness, by combining the principles and practices of internal auditing with gemba walks and layered process audits, is great. A company needs to just accept the ideas above, buy into the spirit of internal auditing, gemba walking, and LPAs, buy into what ISO 9004 is really suggesting we do with our internal audit program, and get over the division of responsibilities between quality people and lean people.

Once a company does buy into this, the next question to be answered is, "When we see waste, what do we do with it?"

C. LEAN AND
PREVENTIVE ACTIONS

As stated earlier, if the auditor witnesses waste, the organization needs to determine what to do with that information. Technically, it would be wise to record this waste as a preventive action since the identified waste could lead to a nonconformity and the auditor is trying to initiate action that will prevent that nonconformity from occurring. As an example, if an auditor witnesses a skid of products being *transported* four times to different locations because it is always in someone's way, and yet no value to the product is being added (it is not changing in form) during these four transportation occurrences, then the auditor could and should write a preventive action.

The justification for recording this extra transportation incident as a preventive action is that the extra transportation can easily lead to product that gets dinged, dusty, damaged, or lost, and by doing something about the extra transportation, we are preventing this from happening before it actually does happen.

Some might say, "Well, writing up a preventive action is wasteful. Why not just tell the process team about the waste and have them come up with a lean solution to the problem?" The reason one would not want to do this is because oftentimes the "lean" solution may not fix the problem because the root cause is not known—because root cause analysis was not performed. It is very important to get to the root cause of the problem first, before randomly applying lean tools, in order to eliminate the root cause and the problem.

As an example, let's say that someone came up with a "lean"* solution—without doing root cause analysis—of creating a colored parking space for a skid of components that are targeted for an assembly. After a week or two it is witnessed that the material handlers are not putting the components in the parking space because it is full so they are placing them anywhere they can find an open spot, just like they used to do, and the additional wasteful movement of components is occurring once again.

If, however, they had done root cause analysis by digging deeper and continuing to ask "why?" at each level, they might have found out that the preceding department is encouraged and rewarded to make as many components as possible regardless of whether the process area of interest needs them (it is a "push" system rather than a "pull" system). Or they might have found out that the material handlers are evaluated on how much product they move throughout the day. The more they move, the better their evaluation. In either case, no matter how many colored parking spaces, this "lean" solution will never work until the above possible root causes are addressed.

The other problem with not recording the observed waste as a preventive action is that there will be nothing in the system to ensure that "verification of effectiveness of the actions taken" has taken place. An ISO 9001–compliant preventive action system ensures that verification of effectiveness takes place. The follow-up is necessary to see if the potential problem has been eliminated or minimized.

On the other hand, one might argue that they do not have the resources to do root cause analysis for every wasteful activity witnessed. This is also understandable. But the team and your company have to understand the

---

* I put the word "lean" in quotes because that's how people would interpret this type of action, when in fact it's not just a "lean" solution but also a "quality" solution since the two terms are really one and the same.

ramifications and the risks associated with not doing root cause analysis properly, and then make an informed decision. Perhaps the team or organization should establish guidelines or criteria as to when a preventive action is initiated.

What Requirement Is Not Being Met?

For a long time, I have suggested that a company needs to have a field on its corrective/preventive action form that is called "Requirement" or "Requirement Actually or Potentially Not Being Met." It has been my experience that about 50 percent of the companies I've worked with that have an established corrective/preventive action system have this field and 50 percent do not. If yours does not, I would strongly recommend that it be added. The reason this field is necessary is because it is important for everyone to understand the requirement that is not being met because the requirement itself may be part of the problem. The requirement might be:

- Assumed

- Verbal

- Vague and unclear

- A customer expectation, but not an internal expectation

- Not communicated properly

In the case of a preventive action resulting from wasteful actions, what might be the requirement that is potentially not being met and what is the source of this requirement? Specifically, in the example we've been discussing with the excess transportation of product, what requirement is not being met? There is no requirement in ISO 9001 that states, "the organization shall not transport product in excess and shall not transport product unless it is to an activity that adds value." There most probably is not an internal requirement within the company's quality management system of the same type.

So what is the requirement that is potentially not being met? As stated above, excess transportation can lead to dinged, dusty, damaged, or lost product. This could mean that either the organization (1) does not meet its customer or internal quality expectations or (2) does not deliver on time because new product will have to be made.

Now, let's say that this same company has the following quality policy, objectives, and goals:

Quality Policy

The ABC Company will consistently meet or exceed customer expectations by providing products, services, and information of the highest quality, and will do so safely, reliably, accurately, and on time. We will do so by always improving the effectiveness of our processes and quality management system.

Objectives and Goals

1. Decrease time to make customer changes to three days

2. Decrease quality defectives to 400 ppm

3. Increase on-time delivery to 98%

The requirement(s) above that the organization might potentially not meet due to the excess transportation could be recorded on the preventive action form as:

The ABC Company will consistently meet or exceed customer expectations by providing products . . . of the highest quality, and will do so . . . accurately, and on time.

and/or

Decrease quality defectives to 400 ppm

and/or

Increase on-time delivery to 98%

Requirements for preventive actions can be found in the following documents, and perhaps even more, within your facility:

1. Quality policy

2. Environmental or safety policies

3. Objectives and goals

4. Business plan

5. Customer contracts or POs

6. Company-stated values, principles, vision, or mission

It is wise to quote requirements from these documents because it gives them more meat and meaning when we witness and record potential nonconformities based on what we do not live up to, as seen in actual practice.

D. INTEGRATING LEAN WITH QUALITY PLANNING

Quality Planning

ISO 9001:2008 clause 7.1, Planning of product realization, states:

> The organization shall plan and develop the processes needed for product realization . . . .
>
> In planning product realization, the organization shall determine the following, as appropriate:
>
> a) quality objectives and requirements for the product;
>
> b) the need to establish processes and documents, and provide resources specific to the product;
>
> c) required verification, validation, monitoring, measurement, inspection and test activities specific to the product and the criteria for product acceptance;

The question that one must ask oneself is, "Do these product realization planning requirements have anything to do with lean, and if they do, what is that relationship?" The answers are a resounding "Yes!" and "See below."

Value stream mapping is an activity that is typically done on an already existing process that has abundant waste. It is oftentimes the first step in trying to identify and eliminate waste.

A *value stream* is the set of all actions (both value-added and non-value-added) required to bring a specific product or service from raw material through to the customer.

Dan Jones and Jim Womack define value stream mapping as "the simple process of directly observing the flows of information and materials as they now occur, summarizing them visually, and then envisioning a future state with much better performance."[6]

The key phrase in this definition is "as they now occur." The process already exists. And this, of course, has produced benefits to many companies. But wouldn't it also be wise if value stream mapping were done *ahead* of time, prior to introducing waste into a new system? Wouldn't it be best if VSM were done *during quality planning* in perhaps some of the following instances?

1. Introduction of a brand-new product line

2. After the purchase of a company or production line

3. Moving to a new facility

4. A modification to a product line

5. Merging of two buildings/organizations

To illustrate how lean concepts can relate to quality planning, the planning of product realization process requirements is recorded below once again, and the corresponding lean concepts or tools are shown in parentheses immediately after:

> *The organization shall plan and develop the processes* (future value streams) *needed for product realization* . . . .
>
> *In planning product realization* (A3), *the organization shall determine the following, as appropriate:*
>
> a) *quality objectives and requirements for the product;* (first-pass yield, inventory turns, overall equipment effectiveness, throughput, lead time, on-time delivery)
>
> b) *the need to establish processes* (future value streams) *and documents* (leader standard work, standard work, job breakdown sheets, visual controls, kanbans), *and provide resources* (job instruction training, 5S layout) *specific to the product;*
>
> c) *required verification, validation, monitoring, measurement, inspection and test activities specific to the product* (quality at the source, mistake-proofing) *and the criteria for product acceptance;* (visual controls, job breakdown sheets)

ISO 9001 requires forward planning, a process that typically is not done very well in many organizations, as witnessed by the all too common occurrence of poor new product startups.

Typically, when I teach and consult for others in planning for product realization (sometimes also known as quality planning), I describe its two extremes. One extreme is the day-to-day planning that may occur in the production planning department. The other extreme would be the large project that requires quality planning and might occur perhaps two to six times a year. The project might involve the introduction of a new or modified product line, new piece of equipment, a new building, a new process or technology, or a new communications/computer system. In the latter case, I usually advocate the use of a quality planning checklist similar to what is shown in Figure 3.5.

The purpose of this checklist is to force the team members working on the project to think of as many things as possible to properly prepare the organization for a smooth rollout of the new or modified product/process/system and to assign actions.

Quality Plan Checklist

Originator: _____

Date: _____

Section I

Description: _____
Part number: _____
Existing situation: _____

Background info leading to change: _____

Change requested date: _____

Project leader: _____

Section II

Critical characteristics
(That is, functional, dimensional, aesthic)

Specification — Objective — Goal

1 _____
2 _____
3 _____

Section III

	Yes	No	Resp.	Due date	Comp date	Results
1. Do new procedures, work instructions, or forms need to be developed?	☐	☐				
If yes, which ones? _____						
2. Do existing procedures, work instructions, or forms need to be revised?	☐	☐				
If yes, which ones? _____						
3. Is there a need for new equipment or equipment/tooling modification?	☐	☐				
If yes, explain. _____						

7.1-01A Quality Plan Checklist (Rev. 01-01-05)

Page 1 of 4

Figure 3.5 Quality planning checklist example.

	Yes	No	Resp.	Due date	Comp date	Results
4. Is there a need for additional manpower or skills? If yes, explain.	☐	☐				
5. Is there a need for instrumentation, gages, or test equipment? If yes, what? (If yes, add to the Calibration Control Procedure)		☐				
6. Are there additional quality verification needs above and beyond the current process? If yes, explain.	☐					
7. Are statistical methods required for monitoring and control of the process? If yes, what?	☐					
8. Are new drawings or engineering specifications required? If yes, which ones?	☐					
9. Are new packaging materials required? If yes, what?	☐					
10. Do first articles need to be reviewed and approved for either new or revised components? If yes, which ones?	☐					

Page 2 of 4

7.1-01A Quality Plan Checklist (Rev. 01-01-05)

Figure 3.5 *Continued.*

	Yes	No	Resp.	Due date	Comp date	Results
11. Do we need additional suppliers or do our current suppliers need additional capacity? If yes, for what parts/materials and who?	☐	☐				
12. Do we need additional capacity to warehouse new products? If yes, what needs to be done?	☐	☐				
13. Does the computer database need to be updated? If yes, what?	☐	☐				
14. Is any specialized training required? If yes, what?	☐	☐				
15. Do we have the capability to provide data and/or certificates to customers, if required? If not, what is needed?	☐	☐				
16. Will new status indicators or product identification stickers or markings be needed? If yes, what?	☐	☐				
17. Does a preliminary process capability study need to be performed? If yes, what are the requirements?	☐	☐				

7.1-01A Quality Plan Checklist (Rev. 01-01-05)

Page 3 of 4

Figure 3.5 *Continued.*

	Yes	No	Resp.	Due date	Comp date	Results

18. Does testing capacity need to be increased? If yes, by how much and what needs to be done?

19. Does the floor plan need to be (re)designed to:
   a. Minimize material travel and handling?
   b. Facilitate synchronous material flow?
   c. Maximize value-added floor space?
   If yes, what has to be done?

Section IV

Prior to implementation, all of the checklist items must be appropriately addressed. Those signing below have reviewed the plan and results and have verified that the project, processes, or product is ready for implementation.

VP's signature _____ Date _____

Project leader's signature _____ Date _____

President's signature _____ Date _____

7.1-01A Quality Plan Checklist (Rev. 01-01-05)

Page 4 of 4

Figure 3.5 *Continued.*

The reader may notice that the final checklist question is:

19. Does the floor plan need to be (re)designed to:

    a. Minimize material travel and handling

    b. Facilitate synchronous material flow

    c. Maximize value-added floor space

These are all typical lean-oriented issues that should be addressed during quality planning.

Furthermore, the Automotive Industrial Action Group (AIAG) has published *Advanced Product Quality Planning and Control Plan,* commonly known as *APQP.* This manual is supposed to be followed by all automotive suppliers during their advanced quality planning process.

In the book, organizations are encouraged to use the many checklists referenced, many of which contain questions that are of the "lean" variety, all being asked during the quality planning process.

Integrating lean with quality planning is, once again, another example of how ISO 9001 can complement lean efforts, this time by using lean principles earlier in the process in order to be more preventive oriented.

E. WHERE DOES A3 FIT IN?

In John Shook's excellent book *Managing to Learn,* he describes the *A3 process* as one by which the company identifies, frames, and then acts on problems and challenges at all levels, which is perhaps the key to Toyota's entire system of developing talent and continually deepening its knowledge and capabilities.

Furthermore, John explains that the A3 process is a management process, and the widespread adoption of the A3 process standardizes a methodology for innovating, planning, problem solving, and building foundational structures for sharing a broader and deeper form of thinking.[7]

In other words, it is much deeper than a simple problem-solving process that is wholly documented on A3 sized paper (approximately 11" × 17"), as so many people think. It is an extremely leadership-driven development process that would greatly benefit any organization's quality management system, if done the right way.

Though the format can vary from company to company, problem to problem, and project to project, the general format, as shown in *Managing to Learn,* is depicted in Figure 3.6. At each step, the person who is completing the A3 is challenged by his leader, or mentor, on the process that was used. This is a very process-focused approach and opposes the approach,

Title: What you are talking about?

Owner/Date

I. Background

Why are you talking about it?

II. Current Conditions

Where do things stand today?

• Show visually using charts, graphs, drawings, maps, and so on.

What is the problem?

III. Goals/Targets

What specific outcomes are required?

IV. Analysis

What is the root cause(s) of the problem?

• Choose the simplest problem analysis tool that clearly shows the cause-and-effect relationship.

V. Proposed Countermeasures

What is your proposal to reach the future state, target, or condition?

How will your recommended countermeasures affect the root cause to achieve the target?

Nemawashi, concept selection, benchmarking

VI. Plan

What activities will be required for implementation and who will be responsible for what and when?

What are the indicators of performance or progress?

• Incorporate a Gantt chart of a similar diagram that shows actions/outcomes, timeline, and responsibilities. May include details on specific means of implementation.

VII. Follow up

What issues can be anticipated?

• Ensure ongoing PDCA.
• Capture and share learning.

Figure 3.6 Typical A3 format.

which so many of us take, that focuses on the solution found in section V. The focus on the solution approach is much like final inspection. The focus on the process approach is much like assuring "quality at the source," a lean term that means assuring quality as the product/service is being developed. The A3 approach would have a mentor directing questions toward the A3 developer such as "What alternatives did you consider?" and "How do you know your solution is better than those alternatives?" A mentor, or leader, who is confident in the problem-solving process is much more confident in the solution.

A3 and ISO 9001

In the definition above, it is stated that the A3 process "standardizes a methodology for innovating, planning . . . ." So how does this relate to ISO 9001? It directly relates to the quality planning process of ISO 9001 and can be used in conjunction with or as a major part of the quality planning process.

An organization needs to decide, if it is to use the A3 process religiously, how it will fit in with its current quality planning process. Should it replace the current process? Should it be integrated into the current process? When should it and when should it not be used? Should it ever not be used in quality planning? Whatever the company decides, it needs to make a decision and clarify its use within the quality management system.

One might also notice the overlap between the A3 format and the required elements in a corrective and preventive action process, especially with regard to the emphasis on root cause analysis. Once again, an organization needs to decide, if it is to use the A3 process religiously, how it will fit in with its current corrective and preventive action process. Should it replace the current process? Should it be integrated into the current process? When should it and when should it not be used? Should it ever not be used in corrective and preventive actions? Whatever the company decides, it needs to make a decision and clarify its use within the corrective and preventive action process.

F. INTEGRATING LEAN WITH MANAGEMENT REVIEW

Clause 5.6.1 of ISO 9001 states:

> *Top management shall review the organization's quality management system, at planned intervals, to ensure its continuing*

suitability, adequacy, and effectiveness. This review shall include assessing opportunities for improvement and the need for changes to the quality management system, including the quality policy and quality objectives.

5.6.2, Review input, further states:

The input to the management review shall include information on

  a) *results of audits,*

  b) *customer feedback,*

  c) *process performance and product conformity,*

  d) *status of preventive and corrective actions,*

  e) *follow-up actions from previous management reviews,*

  f) *changes that could affect the quality management system, and*

  g) *recommendations for improvement*

One might first wonder if there really is or can be a relationship between lean and management review. The purpose of management review is to determine the suitability, adequacy, and effectiveness of the quality management system.

The first question one must ask oneself is, "Is lean and all of its principles, attributes, processes, and culture, a system that manages quality?" Is lean a quality management system or a part of a quality management system? Many "lean" people, who see themselves as being far different from "quality" people, would most probably say that even the mere thought of lean being a part of a quality management system is absurd. But once again, what part of lean does not help to manage the quality of processes and products? It all does, especially the "lean culture" aspect, which includes leader standard work, visual management, daily accountability meetings, and leadership discipline.

While attempting to land a consulting job to help a Texas-based manufacturer become ISO 9001 certified, I suggested to a group of three executives at dinner one night during the bidding process that lean was a subset of a quality management system. Two of these executives had previously worked for a U.S. company that supposedly had a reputation for being a reputable "lean" firm. They both strongly objected to my assertion, and it almost kept me from landing the ISO 9001 consulting job. I ended up getting it as long as I did not try to integrate lean and the quality management system. As it turned out, the two executives who knew all about lean from their previous company only knew very little. Oh yes, they knew how to implement kaizen events, 5S, some work cells, and a little continuous flow. They even created the new role of kaizen team leader, and no kaizen activities would take place without his involvement (the wrong way of kaizening). In reality, though, they knew little of true lean management, lean culture, and its principles. Their very nature was egotistic and demeaning of others, they couldn't care less about quality, and they used fear to get done what they wished. They had no idea of how to enact "respect for people," which is one of the key pillars behind lean. They were using lean to drive up production at the expense of quality and employee involvement and morale. They were doing what so many anti-quality production people had done before them, only now under the guise of lean.

If it is understood that lean, and especially lean culture, is a major part of a quality management system, then in what way can management review the system for suitability, adequacy, and effectiveness? The answer to this question is found in the development of a lean culture. In David Mann's excellent book, *Creating a Lean Culture,* he details the following four principles in creating a lean culture:

1. Leader standard work

2. Daily accountability meetings

3. Visual management

4. Leadership discipline (including gemba walks)

All of these four principles are completely interdependent. In other words, a company can not choose to use just two or three of these principles and expect to develop a lean culture. They all need to work together.

When discussing daily accountability meetings, Mann suggests multiple levels of meetings—all brief, standing meetings—located near the performance and action boards as defined in the visual management principle. These daily accountability meetings represent a tiered structure of meetings, allowing for some overlap. The first tier of meetings would be led by the team leader and would include the operators or direct reports. The second tier would be between the supervisor, the team leaders, and support personnel. The third tier would be led by the value stream manager and would include the supervisors and support personnel. The objective of the meetings, to varying degrees, would be to ensure that standard work is being followed, to review the results from the previous day, including the reasons for misses (that is, missed expected results for an hour time period), to assign and post actions (as part of visual management), and to follow up on actions previously assigned.

So the question once again is, "How does this relate to the management review?"

It is unquestionable that a value stream manager is part of "top management" as is stated in ISO 9001! Also, under leadership discipline, the gemba walk is fully described, and it is strongly suggested that the gemba walks be performed by "top management."[8]

Furthermore, the word "daily" in daily accountability meetings is a "planned interval," and the purpose of these meetings is to assess the suitability, adequacy, effectiveness, and opportunities for improvement of the system, whether one calls it a quality management system, a lean system, or a lean QMS or a yellow-bellied sapsucker.

Furthermore, of the "review inputs" required by ISO 9001, daily accountability meetings indeed address, to some extent:

- Results of audits (if somehow combined with gemba walks as described in the previous section)

- Process performance and product conformity (performance tracking charts and other charts)

- Status of corrective and preventive actions (*kaizen activities* in lean speak)

- Follow-up actions from previous management reviews

- Changes that could affect the quality management system

- Recommendations for improvement

The only item not directly addressed may be "customer feedback."

Most companies view management review meetings as a real pain—something they must do because ISO requires them to do it. They see it as an extra meeting that is not really necessary because they already cover the data/information in other meetings. As a result, they conduct their management review meetings in batches of once a quarter or even once a year. They do not even consider that ISO 9001 has no requirements on frequency or length or how the meeting is divided up throughout a year. The frequency of reviewing each topic or "review input" and the format and attendance are up to the organization to define. ISO 9001 does not state that all of the topics must be covered at the same time and at the same frequency.

A typical ISO-minded individual might have a difficult time understanding the above relationship between management review and lean culture. Lean believes in management review, but not in once-a-year batches. It believes in continuous, not continual, management review, and thus it advocates daily accountability meetings with frequent gemba walks, as dictated on leader standard work, while using visual management techniques.

For more information about how top management and CEOs still do not get ISO 9001, refer to the published article in Appendix E, "Ten Signs Your CEO Still Has No Idea About ISO 9001 (and Maybe Lean)."

G. INTEGRATING TARGETS WITH QUALITY OBJECTIVES

In clause 5.4.1, Quality objectives, of ISO 9001, it is stated:

> *Top management shall ensure that quality objectives, including those needed to meet requirements for product, are established at relevant functions and levels within the organization.*

In many value stream mapping kaizen events, one of the last steps taken after developing the future value stream is to develop the targets for the process. Targets, which are basically the same as objectives and goals, are oftentimes summarized onto a target sheet that may look like is the example shown in Figure 3.7.

Many of these targets are quality objectives or directly affect quality objectives. As a value stream mapping kaizen event occurs, it is wise for the organization to ensure that targets and quality objectives are one and the same and that there are no conflicts between them.

H. INTEGRATING TWI WITH JOB COMPETENCY REQUIREMENTS

When the 2000 edition of ISO 9001 was released, there were many positive changes, including the need to focus in on the process. One such change that was seen as being very positive was in the area of employee development.

In the 1994 revision of ISO 9001, it was required that employees receive training. It could be good training, mediocre training, or bad training; it really didn't matter. The employee could have been asleep in class or wide awake. The employee could have learned the job very well or learned nothing at all. This really didn't matter either. All that really mattered was that the employee received training.

Then the 2000 edition of ISO 9001 came out and all that changed—or at least it should have.

Target Sheet					
Item	**Start**	**Target**	**Actual**	**Difference**	**Percent increase/ decrease**
Space (sq. ft.)					
Inventory (RGs)					
Walking distance (Feet)					
Number of handoffs					
Number of people involved					
Customer satisfaction results					
Cycle time					
Full-time equivalent crew					
Productivity					
Changeover time					
First-pass yield					
Scrap rate					
Units/labor hour					
Cost/piece					
5S rating					

Figure 3.7 Value stream mapping target sheet example.

Section 6.2.1 of ISO 9001:2000 was changed to:

Personnel performing work affecting product quality shall be competent on the basis of appropriate education, training, skills and experience.

"What?" some people thought, "Our employees now have to be competent? How is that going to happen?"

Furthermore, section 6.2.2 of ISO 9001:2000 was changed to:

The organization shall

  a) determine the necessary competence for personnel performing work affecting product quality,

> b) *provide training or take other actions to satisfy these needs,*
>
> c) *evaluate the effectiveness of the actions taken*

The 2008 edition of ISO 9001 differs slightly in the wording, but keeps the same intent and meaning.

"These ISO guys are crazy," some people thought, "How are we ever going to ensure that our employees are competent *and* still run a business?"

And yet, it is so ironic how many times employees will record "poor training" as a "root cause" to a nonconformity resulting in a customer complaint. I surrounded the phrase "root cause" with quotation marks because even though employees state that poor training is a root cause, it really is not. "Poor training" is, in essence, blaming a person—the trainer. It is not blaming the training system, which is the real culprit.

A typical action recorded and taken as a result of "poor training" is "retraining," which of course does nothing for the long-term good of the company, and the problem will eventually rear its ugly head again. Why? Because the system did not change! The "retraining" will most probably be exactly the same training that occurred in the first place.

If a company had performed a good root cause analysis in the first place and kept digging down further by continuing to ask why the training program was ineffective, it might have discovered some of these possible root causes:

- No allocation of training resources and time because it's not important.

- Trainers not knowing how to train because there is no system.

- Trainers do not see trainees do the job effectively.

- Work instruction format is too complex.

- Many trainees are learning disabled, dyslexic, or speak another language, and the written and verbal words are not enough to help them understand.

- There is no training plan.

- There is no follow-up plan.

- There is nothing in the system to hold trainers accountable for their training actions.

- Trainers are not given feedback.

- Trainers only show how to do something once.

- Trainees do not understand the importance of each major action because it is not recorded anywhere on the work instruction.

For the most part, these root causes are blaming the training system. The actions to take, therefore, would be focused on improving the training system.

Even though the ISO 9001 standard was improved to include competency requirements, most companies I've seen have done very little, if anything, to really improve their training system and meet the spirit of what ISO 9001 attempted to get us to do. Most registrar auditors accept very little evidence of ensuring employee competency and let most companies get by without a word mentioned.

Let's face it. There are still way too many organizations out there who think of training as putting a new employee out in the trenches watching the best person do the work, and then allowing the new employee to work on their own after a few days of watching.

The good news is that there is good news in the name of Training Within Industry (TWI). Specifically, the Job Instruction module of TWI addresses all of the root causes listed above and does so without blaming the trainer or trainee. I must provide to you a little historical information about TWI before showing the relationship between TWI and the ISO 9001 requirements.

TWI—Born Out of a Crisis

The U.S. government created the TWI Service in August of 1940 as a means of supplying the Allied Powers with the arsenal to defeat Hitler's forces. At this time, the United States was just exiting from the Great Depression. Unemployment was still high, and production capability was low. Supervisors and lead men were in short supply because they were enlisting or being drafted into the military. The world was in a crisis, and yet most Americans did not want the United States to enter into the war because of its own weaknesses at that time.

The purpose of TWI was to increase productivity and allow the United States to become, as Franklin Roosevelt referred to it, the "arsenal of democracy." This, he thought, would win the war without having to enter the war. Of course, we did enter the war, and by 1942 approximately 6000 new workers were entering the U.S. workforce every day to supply this required arsenal for all the Allied forces, including those of the United States.[9]

In 1945, the crisis was over. The United States had the strongest and largest production facilities in the world. The U.S. government disbanded the TWI Service when the war ended. TWI soon died within the organizations that had successfully used TWI as soon as the soldiers returned to their jobs.

The United States exited from the crisis in 1945 and was at the top. Japan had exited World War II at the bottom. *Japan* was now in a state of crisis. Several members of General MacArthur's staff were intimately aware of the benefits of TWI and thought it would be beneficial to teach it to Japanese industry. However, they were not just interested in teaching the *tools* of TWI, but also the democratic *principles* behind TWI, such as "Treat people as individuals." There was an ulterior motive to what General MacArthur wished to do. By helping the Japanese become more productive and improve their economy, he could also teach the *principles* of TWI and thus reestablish Japan as a democratic nation.

Many people strongly believe that TWI and its four modules were the roots of the lean movement. Many people today believe that TWI is the missing link that keeps companies from enjoying true success in their lean endeavors.

TWI is composed of four modules: Job Instruction, Job Methods (the origin of kaizen), Job Relations, and Job Safety.

It is the first module, Job Instruction, that will be addressed in this book because of its profound effect on employee competency. It is a way, a very good way, of ensuring competent employees and should be ingrained into the culture of any organization that is truly serious about living in the spirit of ISO 9001 and lean.

In no way is this an attempt to explain how to perform Job Instruction training. The reader is provided a synopsis of Job Instruction training so that you will know of its relationship to quality management system documents and job competency. To gain more in-depth knowledge of Job Instruction and all of TWI in general, the reader is encouraged to read Donald Dinero's excellent book *Training Within Industry: The Foundation of Lean.*

There are two main elements of the Job Instruction module that impact job competency directly: the document itself, called a *job breakdown sheet* (JBS), and the method of training an employee.

Job Breakdown Sheet

A typical job breakdown sheet is shown in Figure 3.8.

The first column is called "Important steps" and represents the "what." It is a logical segment of the operation where something happens to *advance the work.* The key words are "advance the work." Entering data onto a control chart does not advance the work, so it would not be included on

Description:		
Parts:		
Tools and materials:		
Important steps	**Key points**	**Reasons**
What: A logical segment of the operation where something happens to advance the work	**How:** Anything in a step that might: 1. Make or break the job 2. Injure the worker 3. Make the work easier	**Why:** Reasons for the key points
1.		
2.		
3.		
4.		
5.		
6.		

Figure 3.8 Job breakdown sheet example.

a typical job breakdown sheet, but it would be included perhaps in a work instruction that an organization might typically have in its quality management system.

The second column is called "Key points" and represents the "how." It is defined as anything in a step that might:

1. Make or break the job

2. Injure the worker

3. Make the work easier

It contains the information or data that directly impacts quality or safety.

The third column is called "Reasons" and represents the "why." It is defined as the reasons for the key points. It provides understanding to the employee as to why the key points are so key, rather than just telling an employee to do something without their understanding.

If a company is ISO 9001–certified and already has work instructions, they may get concerned about adding new documents in the form of job breakdown sheets. This runs counter to what was discussed in Chapter 2. A management representative might think, "We already have procedures and work instructions, and now we're going to add job breakdown sheets. That's not a lean QMS!" "Lean" people and some TWI experts might contend that JBSs don't have to be controlled because, after all, they just represent the training notes of the trainer. That argument is silly. What is contained in a JBS, especially the "Important steps" and "Key points," is critical to the quality of the product or service and therefore needs to be controlled.

Patrick Graupp of the TWI Institute suggests, "The JI breakdown sheet can be seen as an addendum or attachment to the SOP, and can be controlled in the same manner. If the SOP changes, then the method of instruction must also be updated to reflect those changes."[10]

As discussed in Chapter 2, the main rule that I always try to follow is "never repeat a requirement or specification." The reason for this is that it is redundant and wasteful, and if there are redundant requirements stated in multiple documents, someone has to remember to change the SOP and the JBS. That is subject to failure.

Depending on the complexities of one's business, it is suggested that the organization consider the different options available to them with the goal in mind that no information is repeated from one document to another document, so that if and when there are changes that are necessary, the change only has to be made once. The other goal is that whatever document exists in the end, it is a controlled document. The alternatives for an ISO

9001–certified company that wants to use JBSs as part of its TWI program and wishes to achieve these goals are:

1. Replace work instructions with JBSs.

2. Modify work instructions to include JBS attributes.

3. Integrate the two as one of my clients, a Nissan supplier, did (see Figure 3.9). Observe that in the last column, this company included "Visual assistance," which contained photographs of the process activities.

The Method of Training an Employee Using the JBS

As a reminder, this section of the book is not intended to provide step-by-step training in how to perform Job Instruction training. It is only an overview of TWI's Job Instruction module and is only intended to show the reader how TWI can complement ISO 9001's requirement for ensuring employee competency.

The process used to train someone on a job function using the JBS is:

1. Instructor tells the worker how many steps are involved.

2. Instructor performs each step and explains out loud each important step.

3. Instructor once again performs each step, but this time explains each step and key point.

4. Instructor once again performs each step, but this time explains each step, key point, and reasons for key points.

5. Instructor assesses worker's readiness to try the job.

6. Worker performs job silently. Instructor corrects any errors immediately.

7. Worker performs correctly.

8. Worker performs job again while stating important steps.

9. Worker performs job again while stating important steps and key points.

10. Worker performs job again while stating important steps, key points, and reasons for the key points.

X USA Corporation						Rev. date:	2-Aug-07
Document number:			Rev level: A				
Document name:						Approval:	
Operation:		Process:		Part/rev. level or machine:			Page 1 of 1

Critical point type legend

Responsibility: Operator

♦ Safety   ☺ Ergonomics   ⊕ Quality   ☑ Best practice

No.	Statement of operation	No.	Important steps	Type	Critical points	Reason for critical point	Visual assistance

Reaction plan for abnormal situations and special circumstances

Tools:

Safety equipment:

Figure 3.9 Combined work instruction/job breakdown sheet example.

The instructor makes an assessment of the employee's competency and whether to turn the job over to the worker, and the follow-up phase begins.

TWI's Job Instruction module would be a huge process improvement to most organizations, and it would allow the organization to finally live up to the spirit behind ISO 9001's employee competency requirement and lean.

For more information on why TWI died in the '40s in the United States and why it will die again in your organization unless your company adopts the correct principles, read "Why Did TWI Die in the United States in the Late '40s and Will It Happen Again?" in Appendix F.

4
Leaning Out the QMS Processes

One of the reasons I decided to write this book was because of the popularity of my workshop entitled "Creating a Leaner Quality Management System." The reviews were always excellent, except for two individuals. Even though the material I presented was aligned very well with the course description, two people from two different workshops thought that the course was more about leaning out your QMS processes because that's what the title basically stated. Because of that I changed the title from "Creating a Leaner QMS" to "Creating Lean QMS Documentation" to make it more clear that the class primarily, but not only, concentrated on leaning out documentation.

At the same time, I would have liked to talk to these two individuals and explain that a QMS process is no different than any other process, and if they use value stream mapping (VSM) to lean out production or office processes, there's no reason VSM can't be performed on the document modification process or internal auditing process or any other QMS process. In fact, I have made suggestions to many companies that they should do a VSM on the document modification and approval process, especially if the lead time is measured in weeks. (One such company, a very large FDA-regulated company with 35 sites around the world and corporate-level procedures took up my advice in 2010 and VSM'd this very process. Their current state map showed a 144 business day lead time!! Their future state map is targeted for a 36 business day lead time! That would be a great improvement . . . *and a great start*!) The reason decreasing the lead time on this process is important is because if it takes a typical company two to three weeks to modify and approve a document, many people might think that this length of time is unacceptable and decide to circumvent the system. In other words, most probably they will go ahead and change the process but not change the document.

Management representatives and internal auditors complain about employees not updating procedures and work instructions all the time. It's not their fault; it's the fault of a cumbersome system most probably riddled with waste, which leads to long lead times in obtaining the modified and approved document.

Nonetheless, I decided that I would address some processes that are more related to what might specifically be called a QMS process, and offer pieces of advice to help cut down on some of the waste that may be inherent in an organization's QMS processes. All other processes specific to your organization should be leaned out in accordance with the value stream mapping process. This chapter will give advice on how to lean out some of the typical QMS processes of document control, record control, management review, corrective/preventive action, and internal auditing.

First, however, there needs to be a discussion about waste in continual improvement processes.

A. WASTE IN CONTINUAL IMPROVEMENT PROCESSES

I will stick with the term "continual improvement" rather than the term I prefer to use, "continuous improvement," only because this is the term ISO 9001 uses and most lean companies practice.

The reader must understand that there may be a great deal of waste within and amongst continual improvement processes, which might include Six Sigma, lean, ISO 9001, and remnants of TQM.

There are different internal kingdoms (departments) that are built, and many kings and queens compete for resources and attention. The management representative leads the ISO 9001 effort. The Sensei or value stream manager leads the lean effort. The Master Black Belt leads the Six Sigma effort.

They're all trying to do the same thing: improve the company's processes and products. But it's a competition, not a collaboration.

ISO 9001 has its quality objectives; Six Sigma has it Big Y's and Little y's. Lean has its targets. And the CFO has her balanced scorecard. All are measures of how well the company is doing, but frequently none of them are aligned and related.

Six Sigma uses the DMAIC (define, measure, analyze, improve, control) process. ISO 9001 requires a system based on PDCA (plan–do–check–act). Lean relies on value stream mapping to start the process.

The Lean Six Sigma people don't talk to process engineers unless they have a special colored belt. ISO folks and lean folks don't talk to each other because they're really "quality" folks and "production" folks, and they've been fighting longer then the Hatfields and McCoys.

As a result, organizations build up more walls, and the waste settles in. Someone develops a waste walk form that is almost identical to a corrective/ preventive action form. There's confusion over whether an engineer should just develop a solution and put it in place, or he should start a Six Sigma project, or he should complete a corrective action form or a waste walk form. If he has to start a project, does he need to get the resident expert in place so that it "counts" as a completed project against someone's objectives to complete 30 Six Sigma projects in a year? Does he really have to fill out that crazy paperwork? Isn't that oftentimes wasteful in itself?

With regard to an ISO 9001 QMS and lean, this book should show that the two could and should be fully integrated within an organization, and that the organization should always be looking for waste in their processes.

B. DOCUMENT CONTROL: SPEEDING UP THE MODIFICATION AND APPROVAL PROCESS

In so many companies, the process to modify and approve a procedure or work instruction takes far too long for users to be comfortable with, so they oftentimes circumvent the system, creating inconsistencies between the written word and the actual practice. This problem becomes further complicated as new employees are introduced into the system and trained in the documented procedure, which is different than what the other employees are actually doing, thus creating inconsistencies between employee work activities.

It is not uncommon to see or hear of lead times of two to four weeks to modify and approve a document. This length of time gives the impression to the users of the system that the quality management system is no more than a bureaucracy. Employees make up excuses or reasons why their specific documents do not need to be controlled: they are only "training documents," or they are "for reference only," or they are "lean" documents (that is, job breakdown sheets) that are not part of the QMS. Instead of looking for reasons to *not* control documents that affect the quality of the process or product, employees should be looking for ways to speed up the document approval process and shrink the lead time.

There are three main approaches that can be taken to improve the document modification and approval process. Perhaps any combination of these three approaches can be pursued, or perhaps another methodology that your company comes up with could be pursued. Remember to be flexible in the approach one chooses but unwavering in the principle. The principle in this case is getting rid of the waste.

The First Approach: Value Stream Mapping

The *first* approach, as discussed in the previous section, is to use the process of value stream mapping (including developing the current value stream, identifying the many wasteful activities and kaizen actions to eliminate the waste, and finally developing the future value stream). This is highly recommended and could bear fruitful results. Since this book's intention is not to explain to the reader how to perform VSM, but rather describe how the concept can be utilized to improve the document modification and approval process, we will use a simple example of how the concept of VSM can be used to at least highlight non-value-added words and actions for possible elimination.

A well-written procedure or work instruction is written as a process. In other words, the output of one step serves as the input into the next step. The output of one document serves as the input into the next document. In other words, the procedure or work instruction, when written correctly, *is* the value stream map. If it is indeed written as a value stream map, it is suggested to use it as such and proceed on to the value stream mapping steps of identifying:

1. Value-added steps

2. Non-value-added steps

Normally, there would be a third choice: "Non-value-added step, but required." The "required" step could be a customer or regulatory requirement. To simplify this example, we will not deal with this third choice. We will deal with only identifying non-value-added steps, specifically verbs, in a document control procedure from a real company, shown in Figure 4.1. The non-value-added verbs in this procedure are in ***bold italics***. It is understood that one may dispute what is considered "non-value-added," which is perfectly acceptable. What is important is the open communication about what is value-added and what is not value-added.

"Value-added" is defined as:

1. Those activities that the customer would willingly pay for

2. Those activities that transform the product in terms of fit, form, or function

Procedure	Title: Document Control	
	Doc. No: QAP-105	Revision: 13
	Date: May 26, 2009	Page: 1 of 4

Printed copies are for reference only: shred immediately after use

1.0   *Purpose.* This procedure is intended to ensure that only the most recent revision of Quality Assurance documents for manufacturing products and servicing customers are available to the appropriate personnel.

2.0   *Scope.* This procedure applies to the control of the Quality Assurance manual, Quality Assurance procedures, Quality Assurance work instructions, and forms.

The processes leading into and out of this procedure are defined in the QMS Process Diagram (QAM-100).

3.0   *Procedure and Responsibilities.*

3.1   The Quality Assurance Manager (QAM) and VP of Engineering ensure that they are the only employees other than the IT Department that have "write access" to the "Quality System Manual," "Procedures," "Work Instructions," and "Forms" folders and that they are the only employees with any access to the "Archived QA Documents" folder within the "Quality" folder.

3.2   Any employee may suggest a new or changed Quality Assurance Procedure (QAP) and Quality Assurance Work Instruction (QAW) by submitting a marked-up copy of an existing document or new document using the current format to their Department Supervisor.

3.3   The Department Supervisor reviews the proposed new or changed document for acceptability, *obtains* a "Word" document from the QAM, makes any necessary changes, reviews with the originator, and sends to the QAM for approval. If revision does not require training (i.e., error correction or process exists), *indicate,* "no training required" in Revision Box. Revisions to forms may be handled with the assistance of IT.

3.4   The QAM reviews the document for initial approval and *advises* the supervisor of changes to be made. Reviews the document to ensure:

3.4.1   Compatibility with the ISO 9001

3.4.2   Compatibility with customer and internal requirements

3.4.3   No redundancy with current documentation

3.4.4   That it flows properly from one step to the next

3.4.5   That the change/addition/deletion adds value to the system

3.4.6   Analysis of possible elimination of other documentation (i.e., words, sentences, paragraphs, or entire documents)

Figure 4.1   Document control procedure highlighting non-value-added verbs.

Procedure	Title: Document Control	
	Doc. No: QAP-105	Revision: 13
	Date: May 26, 2009	Page: 2 of 4

3.5   If acceptable, the QAM:

3.5.1   Changes/adds the revised/new document.

3.5.2   **Assigns** a new document number, if necessary, as follows:

Quality Assurance Procedures	QAP-101, etc.
Quality Assurance Work Instructions	QAW-A01, etc. (Accounting) QAW-C01, etc. (Customer) QAW-E01, etc. (Engineering) QAW-H01, etc. (HR) QAW-J01, etc. (Job description) QAW-M01, etc. (Manufacturing) QAW-P01, etc. (Purchasing) QAW-Q01, etc. (Quality) QAW-S01, etc. (Sales) QAW-T01, etc. (IT)
Forms	QAP # (or QAW #) letter (i.e., QAP-105A)

3.5.3   Updates the "Revision Record" section and the Header of the document (not forms). **Ensures** that the list of approvers is accurate and includes the affected supervisors, and makes any necessary changes. Approvers are defined as: QA Manager, Senior Staff Members, if they or their subordinates are mentioned in any step of the document (not forms).

3.5.4   May choose to delete old "Descriptions of Revisions," but must maintain at least the last three change descriptions on the document at any one time.

3.5.5   **Saves** the document with the new Revision date and a "– (Rev) #" at the end of the document number, in the "QMS Pending Procedures" folder on the shared Drive.

3.5.6   **E-mails** a link to the new/changed document to the first Approver defined above, with a request to review and approve the new or changed document within three working days. **Monitors** the QMS Pending Folder to check the status of Approvals.

Figure 4.1   *Continued.*

Procedure	Title: Document Control	
	Doc. No: QAP-105	Revision: 13
	Date: May 26, 2009	Page: 3 of 4

3.6 The Approvers review the document for adequacy and accuracy, e-mail comments, if any, to all listed in the original e-mail or apply their electronic signature and date to the document and save it. Additionally, the Approvers review the Document to ensure there is no redundancy or duplication of efforts. If approved, the Approver forwards the e-mail on to the next Approver on the list. Supervisors can sign for their subordinates in their absence.

3.7 After receipt of the final approval e-mail, the QAM:

3.7.1 Revises the document and Revision Record, if necessary, for grammatical or format corrections.

3.7.2 *Ensures* that the first page of the document has printed on it: "Printed copies are for reference only. Shred immediately after use." (Not forms.)

3.7.3 For forms *ensures* that IT converts the form to an electronic form.

3.7.4 *Moves* the new document to the appropriate folder (i.e., Procedures, Work Instructions, Forms).

3.7.5 *Moves* the previous "electronic" document into the "Archived QA Documents" folder.

3.7.6 Updates the QA Document Master List (QAP-105B), including its Revision Date and locations and/or the Records Master List (QAP-116A) for forms.

3.7.7 *E-mails* affected Department Supervisors informing them of a new or changed document.

3.7.8 *Informs* the purchasing manager of a changed or new document via e-mail when a vendor is indicated on the QA documents "Master List" (QAP-105B).

3.8 Purchasing faxes or e-mails a pdf copy of any applicable new or revised QAWs to affected vendors in accordance with the QA Document Master List (QAP-105B).

3.9 The Department Supervisor reviews the document and Revision Box and *determines* who needs to be trained or retrained in the new or changed document and *ensures* they are trained in accordance with the Hiring, Training, and Qualifying Procedure (QAP-118).

3.10 The QAM *retains* archived documents in the "Archived QA Documents" folder in accordance with the Quality Records Procedure (QAP-116).

Figure 4.1   *Continued.*

Procedure	Title: Document Control	
	Doc. No: QAP-105	Revision: 13
	Date: May 26, 2009	Page: 4 of 4

3.11 Sales & Marketing Controlled Documents are created per
QAW-S04 (Sales & Marketing Controlled Documents) and
maintained in the "S&M Controlled Documents" folder under the
Marketing Drive. The log *is maintained* in accordance with the
Quality Records Procedure (QAP-116).

Revision Record

Rev	Date	By	Description of revision:
11	1-29-09	G. A.	Revised sections 3.3 and 3.9 to address CAPA 1039.
12	3-19-09	R. I.	Revised 3.5.6 by adding monitoring of Pending Folder for status of approvals.
13	5-26-09	R. I.	Revised section 3.6 to address CAPA 1044. Removed IT to review and approve all QMS Documents.

Figure 4.1 *Continued.*

3. Those activities that are only done right the first time (in other words, there could be an activity the customer would be willing to pay for, but not a second time)

"Non-value-added" is defined as the opposite of the above. Possible examples of non-value-added action words (verbs) are in **bold italics** in Figure 4.1.

Again, a team of people may disagree with what is considered value-added and non-value-added, which is fine. What is important is to identify and agree on at least some of the obvious non-value-added words/ actions and look for ways to eliminate the actions that they represent.

The Second Approach: Root Cause Analysis

The *second* approach is to go straight to root cause analysis. The simple approach is to dig deeper and deeper into the issue by asking "why?" to each previous answer until the system is blamed. Some suggest that asking "why?" about five times is the right amount to get to a systemic cause, though this number can vary. It must be remembered that oftentimes there are multiple root causes to any one problem.

As a bit of assistance to the reader, some possible root causes as to why a document may take so long to modify and approve include:

• There are too many approvers identified in the system

• There are inappropriately identified approvers in the system

• There are no real process owners/value stream managers because the organization primarily operates as departments

• There is no approval back-up system

• The process is not monitored and is therefore not a priority

• A manual, serial system of approval is used

By determining the root cause(s) of a slow process, corrective actions can be put into place, and the process can be sped up appropriately so that lead times are reduced drastically.

The Third Approach: SMED

The *third* approach that can be taken to improve the lead times of modifying and approving documents is by using the concepts of *quick change-over* or *single minute exchange of dies* (SMED). As it is defined in *Quick Changeover for Operators: The SMED System*:

> *The SMED system is a theory and set of techniques that make it possible to perform equipment setup and changeover operations in under 10 minutes—in other words, in the single minute range. SMED was originally developed to improve die press and machine tool setups, but its principles apply to changeovers in all types of processes.*[11]

But can it be applied to the document modification and approval process? The "D" in SMED stands for "die," but can it stand for "document"? If we are interested in reducing the amount of time it takes to modify and approve documents, isn't this the same thing, in principle, as reducing the time it takes to modify and approve a machine setup?

There is one key difference. A machine setup *must* be modified and approved prior to running more product, but a document need not be modified and approved before the change in a process is enacted. In other words, people can change the process before changing the documented process, and they do. There is a real danger in doing so related to inconsistencies in how people perform their actions and the fact that if one does not have to wait for the documented process to be modified, then the modification of the document itself becomes a very low priority, as it has in many companies.

So if it is agreed that processes should not be changed before the documented process is changed, then it becomes a wise goal to reduce the time it takes to modify and approve a document.

The typical basic steps in a setup operation and the proportion of setup time spent on each step are shown in Figure 4.2.

Since the words in this table, without doubt, refer to machine-related changeovers, it is necessary to change the wording of the four-step process to relate to the document modification and approval process.

Steps in setup	Proportion of setup time before SMED improvements
Preparation, after process adjustments, checking of materials and tools	30%
Mounting and removing blades, tools, and parts	5%
Measurements, settings, and calibrations	15%
Trial runs and adjustments	50%

Figure 4.2 Basic steps and proportion of time spent in each in a typical setup operation.

Source: Shigeo Shingo and Productivity Press Development Team, *Quick Changeover for Operators: The SMED System.* New York: Productivity Press, 1996.

Step 1: Preparation, After Process Adjustments, Checking of Materials and Tools. This step would normally refer to ensuring that all parts and tools are where they should be and that they are functioning properly. Also included in this step is the period after processing when these items are removed and returned to storage, machinery is cleaned, and so forth. To make this more "document" friendly, the title of this step in our application is now called *Preparation, after approval changes, checking out existing documents.* It will include the time it takes to ensure that the document identified to be modified is indeed the latest edition of that document and that the latest edition is in all controlled and uncontrolled (if applicable) locations. It will also include the time taken to destroy or move the obsolete document to its proper archived location.

Step 2: Mounting and Removing Blades, Tools, and Parts. This step would normally refer to the removal of parts and tools after one lot is processed and the attachment of the parts and tools for the next lot. Generally, the machine must be stopped to do this step; this is called *internal setup.* This step, the actual changing over, takes very little time compared to the other steps. To make this more "document friendly," the title of this step in our application is now called *Changing words, paragraphs, references, document control features, and revision record.* It will involve just that, and it will generally take up the smallest percentage of time compared to the other steps.

Step 3: Measurements, Settings, and Calibrations. This step would normally refer to all the measurements and calibrations that must be made in order to perform a production operation. Although the equipment must often be stopped for this step, the SMED system teaches ways to do these tasks quickly by preparing while the equipment is still running. To make this step more "document friendly," the title of this step in our application is now called *Review and approval.* It will involve the reviews and approvals of all personnel directed to do so, no matter how many there are . It will also involve the process of revising the modified document and going through the review and approval process again.

Step 4: Trial Runs and Adjustments. In the final steps of a traditional setup operation, adjustments are made after a test piece is machined. The more accurate your measurements and calibrations are in the previous step, the easier these adjustments will be. This step accounts for about half the time in a traditional setup. SMED teaches ways to eliminate this step completely, so that the machine makes good products right after it is started up. To make this step more "document friendly," the title of this step in our application is now called *Post training modification to documents.* It will involve the time taken to once again modify the document after employees who have been trained in the newly modified document point out that the modified documented process is either incorrect, inefficient, or ineffective.

Figure 4.2 is now modified to Figure 4.3, which now includes the titles of the steps more specifically related to the document modification and approval process.

It would be up to one's organization to monitor and measure each step as it specifically relates to its own process and then complete the right-hand column of Figure 4.3. The steps themselves may also change in name or scope depending on each organization's specific process. With this realization of how time is spent, an organization can proceed from this point and improve the very important process of document modification and approval.

The main reason changeovers take so long is due to the confusion between *internal* and *external setup* and how to treat them uniquely in order to reduce changeover time. In a traditional quick changeover improvement event, the focus is on minimizing the time that a machine is down and not producing parts or materials. In the case of a document modification and approval process, there is no procedure that is inactive. Either 1) the existing procedure continues to be used until such time that the new procedure is approved, people are trained, and it is in effect, or 2) the supervisor responsible for the modification determines that the actual process change can not wait for the approval process to be completed, so she enacts the change before the document is changed, or 3) there is some hybrid of the first two options, and inconsistencies are prevalent. One way or the other, with either of these possibilities, confusion prevails as the process is in a state of limbo. It is this period, much like the time period in which a machine is not producing product, that is the focus of time minimization

Steps in setup	Proportion of setup time before SMED improvements
Preparation, after approval changes, checking out existing documents	?
Changing words, paragraphs, references, document control features, and revision record	?
Review and approval	?
Post training modification to documents	?

Figure 4.3   Setup steps in the document modification and approval process.

as we proceed through the quick changeover of the document modification and approval process.

There are three main stages that occur, and while this is not a book written with the intention of providing the reader with the "how to" of the quick changeover or SMED system, the intent is to provide the reader with examples and the sense of how this methodology can be applied effectively to improve any company's document changeover system.

Stage 1: Separating Internal and External Setup. The most important step in implementing SMED is making a distinction between internal and external setup activities. By doing some obvious things like preparation and transport of the different items required during the changeover while the machine is running, the time needed for internal setup (with the machine stopped or, in our case, the document being in limbo) can usually be cut by as much as 30 to 50 percent.

So the question is, in our specific case, are there certain internal setup steps (while the document is in limbo) performed that can be done externally (before or after the document is in limbo)? Let's examine the previous document control procedure in Figure 4.1. The document is basically in limbo from step 3.3 to step 3.9. Any of the actions between steps 3.3 and 3.9 are considered internal setup steps. The following actions could perhaps be moved to either before or after this internal setup time while the document is in a state of limbo, thus decreasing the overall "limbo time" of the document modification and approval process:

3.7.4   Moves *the new document to the appropriate folder (i.e., Procedures, Work Instructions, Forms).*

3.7.5   Moves *the previous "electronic" document into the "Archived QA Documents" folder.*

3.7.6   *Updates the QA Document Master List (QAP-105B), including its Revision Date and locations and/or the Records Master List (QAP-116A) for forms.*

Stage 2: Converting Internal Setup to External Setup. To continue to further reduce setup times, there are two important steps that need to take place: 1) reexamining operations to see whether any steps are wrongly assumed to be internal setup, and 2) finding ways to convert these steps to external setup. Operations can often be converted to external setup by looking at their true function.

One example of this is found in the following paragraphs:

3.5.3   *Updates the "Revision Record" section and the Header of the document (not forms).* Ensures *that the list of approvers is accurate and includes the affected supervisors, and makes any necessary changes. Approvers are defined as: QA Manager, Senior Staff Members, if they or their subordinates are mentioned in any step of the document (not forms).*

and

3.6 *The Approvers review the document for adequacy and accuracy, e-mail comments, if any, to all listed in the original e-mail or apply their electronic signature and date to the document and save it. Additionally, the Approvers review the Document to ensure there is no redundancy or duplication of efforts. If approved, the Approver forwards the e-mail on to the next Approver on the list. Supervisors can sign for their subordinates in their absence.*

It could be questioned as to whether it is necessary to have all senior staff members as approvers. Perhaps most or all senior staff members *need to be aware* of the changes for training purposes, but all do not have to actually be approvers. This could especially be true if an actual "process owner" exists—a person who is truly accountable and responsible for the procedure. In this case, we are reexamining the purpose of the approval activities. Perhaps the process could be changed to e-mailing senior staff members *after* the procedure has been changed, thus converting an internal setup step to an external setup step and decreasing the overall cycle time of document modification and approval.

Stage 3: Streamlining All Aspects of the Setup Operation. To further reduce setup time, the basic elements of each setup are analyzed in detail. Specific steps to reduce setup time are applied, especially to internal setup operations.

In this step we question all activities and attempt to find ways of streamlining the overall process. Examples of how the process could perhaps be streamlined might include:

1. From step 3.6, it was stated, "If approved, the Approver forwards the e-mail on to the next Approver on the list." The process could be changed so that the approvers receive the document at one time, in parallel fashion, rather than the current serial fashion.

2. Step 3.5.2 could also be questioned for its value: "*Assigns* a new document number, if necessary." The team working on this project

determined that assigning a document number was of no value to the users and was not necessary in their system, so the team decided to get rid of the step altogether.

If a company determines that it wishes all employees to use the QMS consistently, it must make the document modification and approval process user-friendly. The reader and his or her team can 1) choose to treat the procedure as a value stream and identify non-value-added actions for possible elimination, 2) use root cause analysis to determine why the process takes so long, or 3) use the principles of quick changeover and SMED to reduce overall time of the document modification and approval process.

C. 5S'ING FILES AND FOLDERS (A LEAN ORDER ENTRY CASE STUDY)

Following is a real case study of 5S'ing customer service order entry files and folders. The same concept of 5S'ing folders and files can be applied to:

1. Quality management system documentation

2. Drawings and specifications

3. Programs

4. E-mail folder organization

5. Databases

6. Records

Lean Order Entry

A very good client (definition: one in which top management actually is open to modifying its behaviors and management structure, one that wants to learn real lean—not practice fake lean) asked me to evaluate why its waste reduction and quality improvement efforts in the order entry process had run into a roadblock and were not progressing any further after some initial successes.

This client, based in Waunakee, Wisconsin, is a manufacturer of gearboxes and motors and is owned by a German parent. Several months prior to this request and just after my providing a simple one-day lean office overview and simulation and referring the students to some good lean books, the president of the company put a team together and led the team through a value stream mapping exercise of the order entry process, a process in which the company was experiencing a high rate of shop order errors coming back from the production floor. *The president had no previous training in value stream mapping but he led the team through a lean exercise and made some real changes—how cool is that? The customer service manager as well as the team leaders were very much on board and not only supported the suggested changes, they drove them.*

So, per their request, I performed a full analysis of their lean environment and waste reduction efforts in the order entry process. This included a gemba walk, or in this case, a "gemba sit" because when "going to see" an order entry person perform his work, it's easiest to see in a sitting position. Also, in the spirit of not becoming overly dependent on Japanese words that make no sense to most employees within the company, "gemba walk" was renamed to "improvement walk."

At the conclusion of my analysis, I presented my observations and recommendations. Like so many other companies, this company had made some nice changes to the process and got rid of some waste but, for the most part, they made no cultural changes or leadership changes that would support and encourage everyday improvement activities. They focused on the lean *tools,* rather than the lean *principles.* They also optimized the department process without looking at the entire system.

Many of the most important recommendations made and presented to this company focused on creating a lean culture. As was so eloquently summarized by David Mann in his book *Creating a Lean Culture,* the four main interdependent facets of creating a lean culture are:[12]

1. Leader standard work

2. Visual management

3. Daily accountability meetings

4. Leadership discipline

I provided a hands-on lean culture class to address all of these facets along with some of Dr. Deming's principles and other leadership principles. The company took all four facets to heart and made real cultural, organizational, and management changes.

Besides the lean cultural changes, one of my more *radical* recommendations was to "5S" the order entry work area and process, including the computer monitor desktop and all of the electronic folders and files. It's only radical because 5S is so infrequently applied to office processes, much less the organization of electronic files. I taught a brief class and we went to work. I asked the participants to think conceptually, since all of the examples I had were more manufacturing related. I also made sure that their main "IT dude" participated, in case we needed his expertise. As it turned out, he was very valuable to the efforts!

Here are the results of the two-day 5S event for this company's order entry process.

1. *Sort*

   A. Order entry personnel have to reference many different documents as they "build" orders into the system. It's a highly skilled position. The documents that the order entry personnel reference were organized into the following folders:

      • Work Instructions

      • Order Entry Screens

      • Product Data Sheets

      • Product Manual

      • Quality Systems Log

      • Reference Sheets

      • Technical Manuals

      • Procedures

   B. An electronic folder entitled, appropriately enough, "Red Tag" was created. The group went through every document in the above folders and if the document had not been referenced in the past month or so, it was moved into the "Red Tag" folder or simply deleted if it was known for sure that it was obsolete. The target time frame to determine a disposition for each of these documents was two weeks. At that point, the Red Tag folder would also be eliminated.

   C. All hard copies of reference documents hung on the cubicle walls, and product manuals that were within the cubicles and not used within the last month or so were also red-tagged (see Figure 4.4). A list of hard-copy product manuals that were deemed necessary to be maintained in the cubicle was created. It was discovered that there was a huge discrepancy between the manuals being maintained within each of the five order entry personnel cubicles.

   D. Unneeded documents on all order entry personnel's computer monitor desktops were moved to the Red Tag folder if they had not been used in the last month.

Figure 4.4 Red tags in a cubicle.

2. *Set in order* (or *straighten*)

A. Persons performing the order entry process were having a very difficult time finding certain documents because of the way they were organized. They were organized by types of documents. If a customer ordered a special gearbox, and the order entry person had to review a reference sheet, she would have to go into the "Reference Sheets" folder. Next, if she had to reference a product data sheet, she would minimize the reference document and go through a number of clicks to reach the "Product Data Sheets" folder and try to find the appropriate document. There might be more documents that this person would have to reference, but because of the difficulty and the inconvenience in finding such documents she might try to rely on her memory, and with so many facts to be kept in mind, errors ensue.

B. Arranging documents by type (that is, procedures, work instructions, forms, reference documents) is no different than arranging the production process by similar types of equipment (that is, all machining operations together, all welding operations together, all assembly operations together) and arranging people by expertise (that is, all engineers together, all customer service representatives together, all purchasing agents together). Arranging documents together by type, not use, is not convenient to the user and thus hurts the most important aspect of business: the process.

C. The group rearranged the folders by product type, which is how they "build" the product description in the computer. The documents that the order entry personnel reference are now organized into the following folders:

- Gearbox

- Motors

- RGAs

- Oil/Paint

- Parts

- Germany Orders

- Etc.

This was a great improvement over organizing documents by similar type as was described above. The order entry and customer service personnel, including those who were not involved in the reshuffling, all claimed that the new organization was so much easier to use. If it's easier to use, then it will be referenced more often, and the quality and speed of developing shop orders will increase.

D. When an order entry person now receives an order for gearboxes, he opens the Gearbox folder and can easily find any document necessary, whether it is a product data sheet, reference sheet, work instruction, or procedure that relates to gearboxes. The process to find documents and enter an order now requires many fewer keystrokes, which should result in fewer errors and a faster process. This was all due to "setting in order" in accordance with how one uses the folders and files.

E. The documents themselves also needed to receive a little setting in order or "straightening." The file names were organized by number and then description, for example, *AA 7.2.1-014 Brake Motor Order Entry*. The number and letters at the beginning of the file name had no meaning to the user, only to the ISO 9001 quality management document control person. So the number was eliminated from the link to the file name, and the files within a folder were naturally organized in alphabetical order. The new file name for the aforementioned document is now *Brake Motor Order Entry*, and since it is now arranged alphabetically, it is much easier to find. Any time a document or product or tool or machine is easier to find, the more chance there is that it will be used and used properly.

F. Viewing all of the necessary documents in addition to the order entry screens is very difficult to do on one monitor. In addition to all of the above changes, a dual monitor system was purchased for each order entry person. Though I would like to credit the 5S process for this much-needed improvement, this was an action that was in place as a result of the earlier efforts to improve the overall system and reduce waste.

G. The icons on the order entry personnel's computer desktops were also properly organized and standardized for ease of use and consistency in training.

3. *Shine*

A. On an ongoing basis, one is supposed to periodically "shine" their process and inspect it for any possible wear and tear issues.

B. A five-minute shine at the end of each work day was instituted in which each order entry person makes sure that the correct electronic and hard-copy documents are in the right place and that they complete the order they are working on before leaving. If three order entry personnel are finished and one is still working on a difficult order, the others lend support.

4. *Standardize*

A. Once the folders and files were set in order, it was easy to standardize on what all of the order entry personnel saw when they entered the main folder. The folders were also electronically locked so that they could not be moved.

B. The hard-copy product manuals, of which there are about nine, are now all standardized for each order entry personnel. A list was also developed for any new person that would arrive into the process so that he would receive the exact same product manuals in the exact same order, which makes training much more consistent. The manuals are organized in a standardized three-ring binder on a platform angled toward the user for ease of accessing.

C. The product manuals now have standardized tabs on the side and across the top of the manuals. Each tab has a specific meaning as identified by color, which allows for ease of opening to the desired section.

D. A portion of the physical desktop within the cubicle was standardized to include five hard copies of frequently used reference documents. Some of these documents have their locations labeled on the cubicle wall to make it more visible if the documents are missing or out of date. The entire desktop was not standardized, just the working portion, to allow for freedom of expression and personnel effects to be displayed in other portions of the cubicle as desired.

E. Additionally, a list was made of all of the required items a new employee would need, which is now part of the orientation checklist.

The results of the first four S's can be seen in the "before" and "after" photos shown in Figure 4.5.

5. *Sustain*

A. This is the most difficult step for every company.

B. However, the changes that were made to support a lean culture and your quality management system provide a much better chance of supporting and sustaining the improvements that were made:

- For example, the team leader's standard work includes a once-a-week check to ensure that all of the standardized electronic and hard-copy documents, the cubicles, and the computer monitor desktops are organized in the same fashion, are where they should be, and are of the latest edition (and in compliance with their ISO 9001–certified documentation system).

- The customer service manager's standard work includes ensuring that the team leader is performing her standard work.

- The president's standard work includes ensuring that the customer service manager is performing his standard work.

Figure 4.5   "Before" and "after" photos showing the results of improvements made with the first four S's.

- The visual controls put in place make all of their standard work that much easier and quicker to perform.

- The daily accountability meetings provide ample opportunity to bring up discrepancies to the team and agree on a resolution.

- The leadership discipline encourages the order entry personnel to develop their own solutions to these and other problems that arise.

The development of a lean culture and an ISO 9001–based quality management system allows for the ability to sustain improvements (resulting from the use of lean tools) and builds discipline and accountability into the system, *unless, of course, top management does not follow its own standard work.*

D. MINIMIZING THE WASTE IN RECORD CONTROL

Being an electronic pack rat is so easy when there is so much storage space available and people are afraid of throwing anything out lest they need it some day. However, there is a real cost associated with being a pack rat. From a May 2007 post on the Evolving Excellence blog:

> *According to a* Wall Street Journal *article, Chevron and Credit Suisse are taking a new approach to data storage. Chevron noticed that digital files (including e-mails) stored on their servers were growing at 60% per year, with negative effects on the business.*
>
>> *Besides the cost of buying new storage systems, Chevron's employees were spending between 1-1/2 to three days a month just searching for the correct information they needed to do their jobs, taking a toll on productivity, the company found. "We haven't adequately managed all our information," says Lynn Chou, Chevron's general manager of global technology and strategy, adding that the 59,000-person company processes one million e-mails a day. "There's been a digital tidal wave."*
>
> *(For those of you who need help with the math, that's from 35–70 minutes per day looking for critical information. Or from 18–36 work days per year. Think about the muda from the customer's*

perspective. Hell, think about the fun stuff you could do with that time.)[13]

Furthermore, an article entitled "The Paper Chase" from the January 4, 2006 edition of *The New York Enterprise Report* states:

> And if you don't think that your crammed-to-capacity filing drawer isn't costing you, consider that in 1997 the Wall Street Journal *estimated that executives waste six weeks per year looking for misplaced information from messy desks and files. Better organization means that you can apply your skills to the most productive and financially rewarding tasks.*[14]

Need more recent data? From a *New York Times* article entitled "Time Wasted? Perhaps It's Well Spent":

> Searching through clutter is another diversion, says Peggy Duncan, a "personal productivity coach" in Atlanta, who maintains that rifling though messy desks wastes 1.5 hours a day.[15]

That's the equivalent of about one day per week . . . or ten weeks per year! It's only going to get worse because it is so easy—in fact, too easy—to save documents and records because it seems that we have unlimited storage capacity. It seems great, until we realize that it is affecting our productivity in the form of searching for documents.

Most record waste exists in the form of excess inventory of records. As in the case of improving the document modification and approval process, it would be wise for an organization to complete a root cause analysis on why so many records exist within their company. Excess inventory of records may result from any of the following possible root causes (beneath each possible example are ways or examples of ways to combat each cause):

1. The company or individuals maintain both electronic records and hard-copy records.

Employees oftentimes maintain hard-copy documents because "that's what we've always done" or "that's the way I was trained" even though electronic copies have been stored since the advent of the computer. Set a company policy to maintain only electronic files and communicate this to all employees. Ensure that the appropriate procedure or work instruction reinforces this policy by stating what a responsible individual is supposed to do with the hard copy (something just short of filing it where the sun doesn't shine). Also, address a policy of not storing multiple electronic copies on individual PCs.

2. Double entry of data. For example, in some companies that use Excel forms for their corrective/preventive action system, most of the data

exists in either an electronic or hard-copy corrective action/preventive action (CAPA) form. However, the management representative or designee desires to keep much of this same information in a log to track progress. She inputs much of the exact same data into the log, thus creating the double-entry phenomenon.

Use electronic databases and get away from paper forms, where possible.

3. Oftentimes, records are not destroyed even after complying with regulatory, customer, and/or internal record retention requirements.

Too often, companies specify minimum retention times to comply with ISO 9001. What they should do is also specify the "destroy date," and record these dates on the outside of the boxes or in electronic files containing the documents, along with the method or reference to a method of destruction.

4. Individuals maintaining additional electronic or hard-copy records above and beyond the "official" records.

Find out why employees are storing their own records. Do a root cause analysis on why they are and under what circumstances. Perhaps the records are hard to find or hard to retrieve. Address this and set up the filing system so that they are easy to find.

5. Treating all records equally (that is, the unimportant records are treated exactly the same as the critical records).

From the *Evolving Excellence* article:

There's no stopping the increase in information, of course. So these companies are changing the way people manage their information:

> *Credit Suisse, for example, began categorizing its data into different "tiers" of importance in 2003, with critical information such as stock-trading information classified as tier-one data while personal spreadsheets might be classified as less important tier-three data. Tier-one data can be accessed at all times and also more quickly than tier-three data "in recognition of the fact that not all data is created equal."*

And Chevron is doing something similar:

> *Chevron's system will require new office documents to be tagged according to their type and importance, such as noting whether the document is confidential, classified, or just informational. As a result, the company expects to*

delete some documents of lesser importance as soon as 90 days after creation.

Although neither company uses lean terminology, they're really applying elements of a 5S program. They're setting standards for sorting and organizing their information so that employees can immediately retrieve the critical stuff. The less-important information—tier-three, or just old reference material—is moved elsewhere or deleted so that it doesn't impair employees' ability to work.[16]

6. There is no one responsible for holding others accountable for record destruction and organization.

Again from the *Evolving Excellence* article:

Toyota applies 5S principles to its employees' files as well. The former president of the Toyota Technical Center in Michigan used to do spot checks of file cabinets to ensure that information was organized properly. And even now a vice president audits each employee's e-mail system to ensure that messages are well organized and that old messages with no value are deleted.[17]

This activity can and should easily be placed onto a leader's standard work document.

Dan Markovitz, author of *The Paper Chase*, further recommends:

The problem stems from the way most people approach their filing: they focus on filing, not on finding. As a result, the documents that they work with most often at any given time—the high-value documents—are buried in an undifferentiated mass with all the other, low-value documents.

The key to resolving this problem is to separate your paper files into three distinct categories:

Working files. *The file drawer in your desk contains your "working" files. This drawer should only contain the files that you use on a daily basis—drafts of a speech you're preparing, a meeting agenda, or a preliminary budget. When these projects are completed, you'll move them into the "reference" file cabinet.*

Reference files. *Reference files will mirror your working files—you'll use the same categories/hanging folders that you have in your working file drawer. However, these files are kept in a separate filing cabinet away from your desk. In addition to obvious reference items like research reports, you might place the annual budget, HR forms, marketing plans, etc., in this file. The key is that these files contain items you don't need to look at every day, but might look at intermittently, say weekly or monthly. When you do need these files to complete a project—say, preparing a new speech—then you move the files into the working file drawer.*

Archive files. *These files should be kept in another drawer in the file cabinet, in a central storage location in the office, or even at an off-site location. They're accessible to you when you need them, but they're out of your way for the 99% of the time that you don't. As with the reference files, when you do need these files for a project, it's a simple task to move them into the working file drawer.*

Finally, your inbox and outbox: both should be dealt with in a similar manner. The inbox, whether for paper or for e-mail, contains only those items you haven't yet read. Once you read something in the inbox, deal with it immediately—forward to the appropriate person, file in the appropriate folder, or trash it. Like the inbox, the outbox is not a long-term storage device. Items placed in the outbox should be distributed or filed by the end of the day.

The 80/20 rule in life applies to your files, too: you do 80% of your daily work with only 20% of your files. Set up this system, use it daily, and you'll save you and your company time and money.[18]

Master Lists

Many organizations have both a *record master list* and a *forms master list* (that may or may not be part of a *document control master list*). Since most forms become records, the forms master list should be a subset of the record master list. There is a strong relationship between the two lists, and because of the redundancies between the two that can exist, errors could prevail. In other words, let's assume that a company maintains an *incoming inspection form*. It is listed as such in the forms master list. However, since it is also a record that needs to be retained, the form's name and document number, and so on, are also recorded on the record master list. The form name and document number are redundant, and therefore a mistake could be made.

Also, if a form is listed on the form master list, then one could easily check to see if it is also listed on the record master list. If it is not, a nonconformity could be issued.

A better way of maintaining both lists is to combine them into one *form/record master list* as is shown in Figure 4.6.

This example contains a few examples of records. The first example is "Calibration certificates from suppliers." There is no form for these records because they come directly from the many varied suppliers. This is why the "Form #," "Revision," and "Location of blank form" fields are not applicable (N/A). Just after the fourth column and prior to the fifth column, "Indexed by," is a dividing line. To the left of the dividing line is the necessary information regarding the blank form itself and to the right is the necessary information regarding how to control the completed form, or record.

E. MINIMIZING THE WASTE IN MANAGEMENT REVIEW

I have always found it very ironic how many ISO 9001–certified companies are also into lean but don't know how to apply the concepts to their own management processes.

For example, lean is about getting away from batch processing and doing things more in a single-piece-flow fashion. One would think that reviewing the effectiveness and adequacy of the management system is something that would be considered to be very important, something that should be done frequently in single-piece-flow fashion, rather than something that would wait to be completed at the end of the year in one big *batch*.

And yet, that is what is done in so many companies. Either monthly, quarterly, semiannually, or even annually, top management gets together for the dreaded "ISO management review meeting" that is done in one big batch because that's what ISO tells us to do.

But ISO 9001 does not tell one to do this at all. The following is a list of *false assumptions* that have been made by many people in many companies over many years:

1. All of the ISO 9001–mandated agenda items (found in 5.6.2 Review input) have to be addressed at the same time at the same meeting.

2. All of the ISO 9001–mandated agenda items (found in 5.6.2 Review input) have to be addressed at the same frequency.

Forms				Records				
Forms	Form #	Revision	Location of blank form	Indexed by	Initial storage location and duration	Final storage	Minimum retention time	Special instructions (that is, protection, retreival, disposition)
Objectives and goals	5.4A							
Training record	6.2-01A							
Quality planning checklist	7.1-01A							
Supplier score card	7.4-01A							
Approved release for shipment	7.5-04A							
Daily inspection record								
Customer satisfaction survey	8.2-01A							
Internal audit schedule	8.2-02A							
Internal audit checklist	8.2-02B							
Nonconforming product report	8.3-01A							
Nonconforming material log	8.3-01B							
Deviation request form	8.3-01C							
Corective/preventive action reports	8.5-01A							
Corrective/preventive action log	8.5-01B							
Management review meeting minutes	N/A	N/A	N/A					
Training effectiveness evaluations	N/A	N/A	N/A					
Calibration certificates from suppliers	N/A	N/A	N/A					
Supplier certifications (i.e., ISO)	N/A	N/A	N/A					

Figure 4.6 Example form/record master list.

3. Management review must be a *meeting*.

4. No other topics can be covered during this meeting.

5. Regardless of whether or not we have already addressed some of these agenda items, we need to cover them again because the auditor is looking for all topics to be addressed in one set of management review meeting minutes.

None of these assumptions are true, including that management review has to be a meeting. It is the last assumption listed above that angers some top management personnel and makes them feel that the meeting is wasteful, and also explains why they dread attending the "ISO meeting."

Once again, before getting rid of the waste in the management review process, a root cause analysis should be performed to determine why top management feels that the meeting, or process itself, is not effective. I challenge the reader to pursue this route.

So, ISO 9001 gets blamed once again for something that is considered to hold up the business of doing business. But it's not ISO's fault that a company's management review process is dreaded. It is the company's process that is at fault because it may have been based on some or all of the above assumptions. I can not believe that any executive would think that what ISO 9001 requires—"Top management shall review the organization's quality management system, at planned intervals, to ensure its continuing suitability, adequacy and effectiveness"—is *not* a good business practice. If all executives within an organization truly believe that this is a good business practice, then they must simply find a way to make it more effective. That's what ISO 9001 is all about!

I have a very simple way of determining whether or not the management review process is effective. I first review the corrective action/preventive action (CAPA) process and the internal quality audit (IQA) processes for effectiveness. If these two processes are not effective in driving improvement, then I know that the management review process is not effective because the management review process should be ensuring effectiveness of the CAPA and IQA processes.

With one of my clients, I recommended that my contact complete a very simple form prior to defining the management review process for their company so that it would not become a wasteful process. Like so many other companies, they already had a vast amount of periodic standard meetings, and this is why I asked them to complete the first four columns of the form in Figure 4.7.

I suggested that they complete the first four columns of the form for two reasons: 1) to determine if there were any redundancies in the current

Current regularly scheduled meetings	Frequency	Attendance	Topics covered	Relationship to clause 5.6 of ISO 9001

Figure 4.7   Current periodic meetings form.

meetings and to determine whether any of the current meetings could either be downsized or cut out altogether, and 2) prior to adding another meeting in the form of an ISO 9001 management review meeting, we wanted to determine whether any of the topics mandated by clause 5.6.2, Review input, were already being reviewed in another existing meeting. If some of the agenda items were already being covered in another meeting, then there might not be any reason to cover the agenda item again in a new meeting. That would be wasteful! Furthermore, for the agenda items not being covered in an existing meeting (for example, audit results) it could easily be determined where it would make the most sense to place those agenda items in an existing meeting. From this information, we completed the last column together and developed the management review process (without adding an additional meeting) as is shown in Figure 4.8.

Relationship of Lean Culture to Management Review

In the spirit of lean, it is best to perform activities in single-piece-flow fashion rather than in large batches. This would include the management review process. After all, it is silly to think in terms of receiving some important customer feedback (one of the mandated agenda items) in March but not reviewing it until the annually scheduled management review meeting in December. This just does not make sense!

When developing a lean culture, it is strongly recommended that the organization hold *daily accountability meetings.* In a typical lean cultured company, there might be three levels of daily accountability meetings: 1) team leader and operators, 2) supervisor, team leaders, and support personnel, and 3) value stream manager, supervisors, and higher-level support personnel. All three meetings share the same features of brevity (no more than 15 minutes), all attendees standing, and the location of the meetings is where the action occurs and not in a conference room or office. The topics of each meeting are somewhat different, but generally the people attending the meetings do review the visual management boards (that is, production tracking boards, reasons for misses, action boards, complaint boards,

---

Procedure	
XYZ Company	Revision date: 05/25/XX Page: 1 of 3 Prepared/updated by: JR

(Controlled copy if this line is printed in red)

Reviewing the Quality Management System

---

1. *Purpose.* The purpose of this procedure is to describe the process of reviewing the organization's quality management system to ensure its continuing suitability, adequacy, and effectiveness.

2. *Scope.*

    2.1 *Breadth.* From the completion of many activities (i.e., Internal quality audits, corrective and preventive actions) which serve as input into the review process to the initiation of the Corrective and Preventive Action Process (QM-BLT-06), the Identify Opportunity Process (IO-BLT-01), or Training Process (QM-BLT-02).

    2.2 *Depth.* This procedure applies to the review of the effectiveness of all processes within ABC Company. The review occurs over several meeting forums that best reflect our internal structure and provide optimum results with minimal waste.

3. *Procedure.*

    3.1 *Responsibility*   3.2 *Action*

    Management representative

    1. Ensures that the regularly scheduled meetings, as listed below, meet the minimum requirements of the applicable ISO 9001 standard and are continually effective in determining the suitability, adequacy, and effectiveness of the quality management system.

Regularly scheduled meetings	Frequency	Meeting leader	Attendance	Topics covered (Relationship to clause 5.6 of ISO 9001)
BLT Meeting	Weekly		BLT	Financial results, HR, resources process issues (5.6.2.c)
BLT Meeting	Monthly		BLT, Management representative, Audit coordinator	1. Changes to the QMS, quality policy, or objectives 2. Audit results 3. Status of CA and PA 4. Receipt and acceptance of meeting minutes for the following meetings 5. Additional actions necessary (5.6.2.a, 5.6.2.d)

Figure 4.8   Reviewing the quality management system process.

		Procedure		
XYZ Company			Revision date: 05/25/XX Page: 2 of 3 Prepared/updated by: JR	
		(Controlled copy if this line is printed in red)		
		Reviewing the Quality Management System		

ABC Quarterly update	Quarterly		ABC, US	Financial reports, new program update, upcoming issues
AIB/ABC business review	Quarterly		ABC Program managers, AIB Category directors	Review current program status and open issues; availability, program launch (5.6.2b)
Program status review	Weekly		BLT, Program managers, Operational staff	New program status
Warehouse update meeting	Weekly		Warehouse staff	Shipping variance, overtime, staff requirements, productivities (5.6.2.c)
S & OP meeting	Monthly		S & M, Operations, Procurement	Sales actuals/Forecast Forecast accuracy On-hand inventory On-hand inventory days supply (5.6.2.c)
Operational staff meeting	Bi-weekly		Operational staff	Processes
Procurement leadership team meeting	Weekly		Procurement leadership	Suppliers, pricing, PLI, SAL, process
Operational drum beat meeting	Monthly		Operations staff	Open issues, process concerns
Engineering staff meeting	Weekly		Engineering staff	Open issues, process concerns
Procurement staff meeting	Monthly		Procurement staff	Suppliers, pricing, PLI, SAL, process

Meeting leader (as defined above)	2. Ensures that all topics are covered as defined above and documented as such, and that the meeting minutes are recorded on the Meeting Minutes Form (F24) within 24 hours of the meeting and distributed to all involved as well as the BLT.
Meeting leader	3. Retains these records and any backup information/data in accordance with the Quality Records Procedure.

Figure 4.8 *Continued.*

Procedure	
XYZ Company	Revision date: 05/25/XX Page: 3 of 3 Prepared/updated by: JR
(Controlled copy if this line is printed in red)	
Reviewing the Quality Management System	

4. *Revision Record.*

Revision date	Description of change	President approval	Process owner approval	Management representative approval	Effective date
05-25-XX	Original				

Figure 4.8 *Continued.*

priority boards) that are located in the production area, and the meetings drive continuous improvement actions.

These are meetings that are more of the single-piece-flow variety rather than a batched meeting at the end of a month, quarter, or year. These real-time meetings occur every single day when the vision of the process is clear, the problems and misses are fresh, and the actions taken are prompt. And there are managers involved. Is this not a form of management review? Yes, of course it is!

These meetings also address, or could address, the ISO 9001–mandated agenda items of:

1. Assessing opportunities for improvement and the need for changes to the quality management system (5.6.1)

2. Customer feedback

3. Process performance and product conformity

4. Status of preventive and corrective actions

5. Follow-up actions from previous management reviews

6. Recommendations for improvement

Though daily accountability meetings may not cover these topics in their entirety or at the big-picture level (for example, status of preventive and corrective actions would only be for that process area), they are indeed covering these topics at the appropriate level on a very timely basis to help make for a much more effective and leaner management review process.

Management Review Meeting Minutes

In whatever fashion an organization does perform management review, it is required to keep records or minutes of these meetings. So, a very short, simple message about management review meeting minutes, or any meeting minutes, is warranted. Avoid double entry! Don't have a high-level executive or management representative record meeting minutes by hand and then upon completion of the meeting type them into his or her computer for distribution. Either 1) record minutes neatly by hand and make copies immediately after the meeting for distribution before it breaks up, or 2) have someone such as a lower-level person type up the minutes at the meeting under the direction of the management representative and immediately e-mail them out at the end so that the meeting members have them upon return to their desks. This will help ensure that assigned actions are fresh in one's mind, and meeting members may even begin taking action on them immediately rather than waiting for the official meeting minutes to be distributed days later, like so many people do.

Also, ISO 9001 requires the recording of decisions and actions. As a way to make the meeting minutes more effective and easier to read, attempt to stick to only recording decisions and actions, and avoid the extraneous fluff (he said/she said) that one oftentimes finds in the meeting minutes that has nothing to do with the decisions and actions themselves. A standardized form to be used at all meetings, like the one shown in Figure 4.9, could be used as a way of mistake-proofing the recording of the meeting minute process.

F. MINIMIZING THE WASTE IN CORRECTIVE AND PREVENTIVE ACTIONS

I have often said that, by far, the corrective and preventive action process is the most important of any organization's processes. If this process is done well, all of the other processes will eventually do well. But there can be a tremendous amount of waste in the corrective and preventive action process itself, and the biggest waste by far is in the form of *defects*. By this, I mean defective corrective and preventive actions that do not net real improvements to the system. They oftentimes are observed as a hastily written form that has the sole purpose of being closed out as soon as possible before it is late or before an auditor sees it, without any regard for its effectiveness.

Examples of Waste in Corrective/Preventive Action

1. *Separate procedures/forms for corrective and preventive actions.* Up until the publication of ISO 9001:2008, I would still occasionally visit a company that had separate procedures and forms for corrective actions and preventive actions because they were *told* that it was necessary by a registrar or other external auditor. This is silly, wasteful, and misguided. The corrective and preventive action processes are basically the same process, they just have different points of origin. The procedure and the form should be one and the same, and this is now supported by Note 1 of clause 4.2.1, General, in section 4.2, Documentation requirements, which states, "A single document may address the requirements for one or more procedures."

2. *Installing separate forms for lean.* As I mentioned previously, the president of an ISO/TS 16949 transmission remanufacturing facility had

Meeting Minutes

Meeting type: _____ Location: _____ Date: _____

Attendance: _____

1. Always review any business, system, and/or product changes within the company that could affect our quality management system and ensure they are addressed appropriately below within the system.

2. Always review recommendations for improvement.

3. Record decisions and actions resulting from this meeting related to the improvement of our management systems, processes, and products/services, as well as the need for any resources (that is, human, training, infrastructure, hardware, software, communications).

4. When necessary, initiate CAPAs using the Corrective and Preventive Action Procedure (   ).

Item #	Decision or action	Actions only			
		Assigned to	Due date	Comments/notes	Status
1	Review status of actions from previous meeting				

Figure 4.9 Meeting minutes form template.

asked me what I thought of his new Waste Walk form, which could be used by any employee observing waste as part of the company's new lean initiative. After reviewing the form I told him that his Waste Walk form was wasteful because it was nearly exactly like his Corrective Action/Preventive Action (CAPA) form. Redundancy is wasteful. I also told him that because of this redundancy, it would confuse the employees regarding which form or system to use.

3. *Installing separate forms for Six Sigma.* If a company is pursuing Six Sigma and is also ISO 9001–certified, there is a great probability that there will be waste in either or both systems. Six Sigma is about problem solving and problem prevention; so is the CAPA system. Six Sigma uses a process called DMAIC (define, measure, analyze, improve, control); ISO 9001 requires that certain steps be followed when doing corrective and preventive actions. Those steps overlap a great deal with those of DMAIC. Again, the problem lies with the confusion generated by having two problem-solving/prevention processes. When confronted with an issue, an employee may not know whether to initiate a CAPA or a DMAIC process.

Since the processes do overlap quite a bit it is recommended to integrate the two into one process to address the confusion. An example of this is shown in Figure 4.10.

As a reminder of what was written earlier, both Six Sigma and ISO 9001 encourage continual improvement, not continuous improvement, like lean does. (In fact, section 8.5.1 of ISO 9001 is titled "Continual improvement"). In other words, Six Sigma and ISO 9001 are project-based and end with "control" or "verification." Lean carries on on with improvement efforts continuously. This is another way a quality management system can benefit from the lean mentality.

4. *Not removing old forms.* I was helping a client of mine, a manufacturer of hydraulic cylinders in two facilities located in Texas and Tennessee, build a QMS compliant to ISO 9001. We were at the point in our project of developing the CAPA system. Before we began in earnest, we searched their electronic files and found, between the two facilities, *eleven* different documents that did some form of root cause analysis. Talk about confusing the employees! A company needs to address this and get down to one good form for doing proper root cause analysis for a corrective or preventive action.

5. *Too many other terms being used.* ISO 9001 refers to *corrective* and *preventive actions* and uses no other terms. Many companies, including registrars, go beyond these two categories and develop more terms, like *opportunities for improvement* (OFI) and *observations.*

Continual Improvement Request Report

C.I.R. no.: _____

Work order no.: _____

Section I—Define
Initiator: Date:
Requirement (i.e., warranty, specifications, dimensions, quality objective, written ISO or procedural statement):
Discovery method: ❏ Customer complaint ❏ Audit ❏ Warranty return ❏ FMEA ❏ Supplier ❏ Management review ❏ In-process ❏ Receiving inspection ❏ Quality planning ❏ Other _____
Document reference: ISO requirement: SCAI document #:
Description of finding (include specific serial #, work #, P.O. #, quantity, failure type, document #).

Section II—Action Assignment and Scheduled Review Dates
Assigned to: _____ Section III date: _____ Section IV date: _____
Section V date: _____ Section VI date: _____
Company (if supplier): _____   Responsible person (if supplier): _____

Section III—Measure
How will the current situation be measured? What will be measured? (Record below or attach a completed Data Collection Plan [F8.5-02])
Tools used: ❏ Check sheet ❏ Flowchart ❏ Scatter diagram ❏ Control chart ❏ Pareto ❏ Histogram ❏ Box plot ❏ Time series ❏ Other ❏ Other
What is the current process sigma? _____
Will pursuing this project add value to the company and help us to achieve our company objectives? Y ___ N ___
Approvals:
Initiator: _____   President: _____
Six Sigma expert: _____   Management representative: _____
Date:

Figure 4.10   Example of combined CAPA/DMAIC form.

Section IV—Analyze

Description of root cause(s) (Reference WI-QMS8.5.2-01):

Tools used: ❏ Fishbone ❏ DOE ❏ FMEA ❏ ANOVA ❏ 5 whys
  ❏ Regression   ❏ Other ❏ Other

Update FMEA? Y ___ N ___:
If no, Severity = ___, Occurrence = ___, Detectability = ___, RPN = ___ (See F8.5.3-01)
Further action required? Y ___ N ___

Approvals:

Initiator: _____ President: _____

Six Sigma expert: _____ Management representative: _____

Date:

Section V—Improve

Possible solutions (Use Concept Selection Process if there is more than one alternate plan and attach)

Tools used: ❏ Mistake-proofing ❏ FMEA ❏ Brainstorming ❏ Benchmarking
  ❏ Concept selection   ❏ Other ❏ Other

Pilot required? Y ___ N ___:
Actions and action plan chosen:

Actions taken:

Results: Process sigma _____ P_{pk} _____ RPN _____

  Other benefits: _____

Approvals:

Initiator: _____ President: _____

Six Sigma expert: _____ Management representative: _____

Date:

Section VI—Control (and Verification)

Quality system documentation changes:
Control mechanisms used (i.e., X-bar and *R* charts)
Who was trained?

Results: Process sigma _____ C_{pk} _____ RPN _____

  Other benefits: _____

Verification acceptable? Y ___ N ___:

Date: Initiator's/management representative's signature: _____

Figure 4.10 *Continued.*

Let's start with OFIs. If an individual identifies an opportunity to improve something, and the company decides not to take action on that opportunity, there is the possibility that a result of some sort will not be as good as it can be. In other words, if we do take action then we are *preventing* that less-than-optimal condition from occurring. Thus, an OFI is the same thing as a preventive action. If your company identifies OFIs within its system, I dare you to challenge the company to identify these as preventive actions by asking what problem or subpar performance might be avoided if the opportunity is acted upon. I think that you will discover that an OFI is really just a preventive action. After all, there is a reason why ISO 9001 does not have a section called "Opportunity for Improvement."

Let's now move on to "observations." When I do stand-up comedy, I define an observation as "a nice way to tell someone that a nonconformity was observed, but they don't have to do a damn thing about it." In other words, when companies do allow for identifying "observations," perhaps during an internal audit, whether or not they take action is completely optional.

In one example, I was performing a process and quality assessment for an automotive parts supplier in the Northeast that was having some serious quality issues. For a short time I reviewed and assessed their internal audit system. What I noticed was: 1) hardly any CAPAs written in the past year, 2) dozens upon dozens of "observations" recorded, 3) about 75% of the "observations" recorded were really nonconformities in which a CAPA should have been written, and 4) hardly any actions taken on any of the identified "observations." In essence, the company identified nonconformities and took no action because of a loophole called "observations" that allowed the employees a way around making improvements. No wonder this company had problems.

In my final report to the organization, I stated that since one of the purposes of the management review process is to ensure effectiveness of the internal audit process and CAPA process, and since these processes were not effective that must mean that their management review process was also ineffective. I was not invited back again.

6. *Preventive actions not being used to eliminate waste.* I'm sure, initially, some people might think that this is not wasteful. In fact, they might further think that it would be wasteful to record on a preventive action form identified waste and all of the other data typically required on a CAPA.

Let me explain once again. If any employee observes waste (that is, overproduction, waiting, transportation, inventory, excess motion, excess processing), the knee-jerk reaction might be to initiate a kaizen activity or kaizen event/blitz. Furthermore, they might immediately decide that 5S, quick changeover, or a total productive maintenance event should be held. The problem lies in the fact that if whatever activity is decided upon does not eliminate the problem or, more importantly, the root cause of the problem, then all the efforts that were made were "waste" in the form of excess processing. This needs to be avoided. Employees should never jump on the first action that comes to one's mind without understanding the problem and the root causes(s) of the problem.

A preventive action using a CAPA form will enforce and ensure that root cause analysis is performed, thus decreasing the possibility of going down the wrong path of an action that does not address the root cause of the problem. The CAPA form will also ensure that whatever actions are taken were effective at eliminating the root cause of the problem.

Excessive Waiting on the Completion of CAPAs

Waiting is one of the 8 process wastes. As a management representative or internal auditor or even perhaps a lean expert who uses the CAPA system, you would know how frustrating it can be waiting on employees to complete their CAPAs by the agreed-upon due date. It is extremely frustrating, and it generates more waste in the form of excessive processing (another waste) manifested in the countless e-mails and voice mails delivered in tracking down and encouraging the completion of the late CAPAs.

Many organizations experience problems with employees completing CAPAs on a timely basis. Oftentimes, on-time completion rates in the 20% to 30% range are quite common. A client of mine, Val-Matic Valves and Manufacturing, in Elmhurst, Illinois, had such on-time completion rates. They decided that one of the root causes to their particular problem was a lack of visibility to the senior staff and others of the status of past-due CAPAs and soon-to-be past-due CAPAs.

Together, with the assistance of their IT experts, we established a way to provide more visibility to late and soon-to-be-late CAPAs for both the assignees (those who were assigned to determine root cause and actions) and the assignee's supervisor.

This company's particular CAPA form is divided into four sections. Each section is completed by a different person. Section I is completed by the initiator. Section II is completed by one of four people who review and assign the CAPAs to the appropriate person, with due dates for Sections III and IV. Section III is performed by the assignee, who determines root cause and actions. Section IV is completed by the initiator, who determines verification of the effectiveness of the actions taken.

The increased visibility was achieved by having automatic e-mails sent from Microsoft Outlook to the assignee for Section III and to the initiator for Section IV when the CAPA is either "due in a week" or "late."

Three examples of these automatic e-mails are shown in Figures 4.11a, b, and c.

(a)

> **From:** George
> **Sent:** Friday, August 21, 2009 11:01 AM
> **To:**
> **Subject:** QM CAPA Alert—Section III Is Due in a Week
>
> QM CAPA Alert—CAPA No. 1100, assigned to Jeff, is due within a week's time on 8/28/2009. Description: Orders shipping direct to third parties in Canada have been including invoices and/or packing slips that show invoiced prices. The only person who should see the invoice is our customer.
>
> There does not appear to be any direction in QAP-115 or elsewhere that notes what paperwork is attached to skids, given to drivers, and/or sent to customs brokers. Somewhere along the way the invoice is being provided to the party at the shipment destination. This should never be the case. The shipping supervisor has been notified as well.

(b)

> **From:** George
> **Sent:** Thursday, July 23, 2009 11:01 AM
> **To:** Bob
> **Subject:** QM CAPA Alert—Section IV Is Late
>
> QM CAPA Alert—CAPA No. 1057, Due: 7/15/2009, is *late* pending final review by Doug. Description: We shipped to the wrong location. All paperwork indicates the proper "ship to" address was in Wisconsin.
>
> We shipped to Beaumont, Texas.
>
> Ref CO 226787 CFR 1193

(c)

> **From:** George
> **Sent:** Wednesday, August 26, 2009 11:01 AM
> **To:** Bob
> **Subject:** QM CAPA Alert—Section IV Is Due in a Week
>
> CAPA Alert—CAPA No. 996 is due for final review on 8/31/2009 by John, and Tim has not yet completed Section III. Description: ABC Company CO 219152, purchased two model xyz's and was unable to use standard T-head bolts for the MJ connection. Spoke with John who suspects the problem may be related to ECN 624 resulting in dimensional changes. Please follow up with Tim and John as necessary.

Figure 4.11   Examples of e-mails sent to increase visibility of late CAPAs.

Additionally, the subject line notices listed in the three examples pop up on one's computer desktop automatically at 11:00 a.m. every day, and one can not proceed with their work before clicking the "OK" button.

Of course, it needs to be pointed out that a company can not measure and monitor percent of CAPAs completed on time without some measure of the quality of the CAPAs completed. In other words, if the objective and goal is only to increase the percent of CAPAs completed on time, the company could eventually achieve the target but at the expense of good corrective actions eliminating the root causes of problems, and perhaps at the expense of new CAPAs being initiated. The prevailing thought is often, for example, "blame the operator and retrain him so that we can close this CAPA out quickly" or "the more CAPAs you initiate, the less likely we will be to achieve our on-time goal." Additionally, those performing the last step, Section VI, Control (and Verification), in this case will feel pressure to accept whatever is given them to help meet the goal.

Excessive Inventory of CAPA Paperwork

A contract machinist company, DACO Incorporated, located in North Aurora, Illinois, grew tired of their inefficient and paperwork-heavy CAPA process. They decided to change the spreadsheet-based CAPA form and Microsoft Word–based CAPA procedure into a Microsoft Access–based database, which allowed the employees much less double entry of information.

As the transformation occurred and the database morphed into the procedure itself, the procedure was downsized. The previous documented procedure in Word had taken about 15 steps, which was later decreased to three steps as it simply referred users to the database, which walked the user right on through the process.

G. MINIMIZING THE WASTE IN INTERNAL QUALITY AUDITING

Much of this topic was already discussed in Chapter 3. What's most important is to eliminate the wasteful techniques in auditing that provide no drive for the organization to improve. Below is a list of a few wasteful internal auditing habits or techniques.

Not Process Auditing

Much ado has been made about the term "process auditing," and many people still do not understand this concept, or perhaps many trainers/

consultant make this process much more confusing than it really is. *Process auditing* is simply about auditing and following each step of a process in the order in which it occurs. It's about observing what is done and determining whether the process:

a. Agrees with procedure/work instructions

b. Agrees with the standard (that is, ISO 9001)

c. Is effective and capable of meeting the *purpose* and *planned results* of the procedure

d. Is wasteful or not

It is not about asking the same stock questions from a standard that most people do not understand. That is wasteful! When auditors ask obscure questions that the auditee barely understands, and the questions are asked in a somewhat random order because of not following the process, there is little value in the audit process.

Batch Auditing

The other major waste in internal auditing is the batching effect, much like in the management review process, in which an area is audited once a year, in one big batch. As we all know, batching is bad, and a once-a-year audit of a process area is really pretty silly when one thinks about it. This topic was covered in much more detail in Chapter 3.

Distinct Audit Forms for Action

The internal quality audit (IQA) procedure should flow into the corrective/preventive action procedure. In other words, somewhere near the end of the IQA procedure, it might be stated, "After the audit team has agreed on which findings require a corrective or preventive action, the witnessing auditor initiates a CAPA in accordance with the Corrective/Preventive Action Procedure (8.5-01)." There is no need to record audit findings on a unique finding form used only for internal audits. This is wasteful. Just have them use the CAPA. A nonconforming process should not be treated any differently than a nonconforming product.

Double Entry

Another area in which there is waste in the internal audit process is the double entry of data. Internal audit information can reside in many different documents and forms, including audit notifications, audit schedules, checklists, CAPAs, and audit reports. In many of these forms there may reside a great deal of redundancy. For example, the scope of an audit might be found in the notification, the schedule, and the report. An organization should review these documents for redundancy and refashion or combine them in such a way that there is no need to double-enter any information. A simple example of combining an audit notification form and audit summary report form is found in Figure 4.12. In this example, the auditor would complete section 1 electronically and e-mail it to those who need to know about the audit, save it, and then to use it again after the audit by completing section 2 and e-mailing it once again as a completed form.

Defective Auditors

Many internal auditors are trained once, in a batch, and then never again. They do not receive feedback from a competent auditor and they have no way of knowing how good of a job they are doing. They may wish to receive feedback on their performance as an auditor as a means of improvement, but there is no vehicle allowing them to receive feedback. This must be changed. ISO 19011, the auditing standard, encourages organizations to provide feedback to internal auditors against a set of criteria. This can not be stressed enough.

In essence, the waste we are discussing here is defects in the form of defective internal auditors. With defective auditors, the entire audit process becomes wasteful. It's not their fault they are defective as auditors. It's the fault of a system that does not ensure that the organization has competent auditors.

I encourage providing feedback to auditors from an unbiased source for the sake of improving the internal auditor skill set and the internal audit process. An example of an evaluation I provided to an internal auditor of a Milwaukee manufacturer is found in Figure 4.13. You will notice that I provided feedback on the checklist questions prepared in advance, on the auditor performance against a set of criteria as well as written feedback, and on the CAPAs that the auditor wrote up against another set of criteria. I prepared the report and then reviewed my feedback with the respective internal auditors.

Audit Notification Form
and
Summary Report

Section I: Audit Notification

To: _____   Date: _____

From: _____
              (Lead Auditor)

The purpose of this memo is to inform you that I would like to audit the

_____ process on _____ (date), starting

at _____ (time). I will be performing this audit with this/these additional

qualified auditor(s): _____. Please let me know if the

timing of this audit will be a problem.

Audit purpose: To determine whether the quality management system
conforms to our processes, procedures, and ISO 9001:2000, and to determine
if it is effectively implemented and maintained.

Audit scope: (Internal procedures and quality manual—ISO section number)

_____

Other References: (Past audit findings, customer complaints, etc.)

_____

Section II: Summary

Associated objectives and goals:

Objective(s)   Goal(s)   Actual (Most recent)

_____   _____   _____

_____   _____   _____

_____   _____   _____

Comments on progress/actions:

_____

Figure 4.12   Example of combined audit notification form and audit
               summary report form.

Procedures audited   CA #s   PA #s
_____   _____   _____
_____   _____   _____
_____   _____   _____

Weaknesses:
_____
_____
_____

Strengths:
_____
_____
_____

Obstacles:
_____
_____
_____

Related processes to audit in the near future due to a potential issue
observed:
_____
_____
_____

Report date: _____

cc: Management representative, other auditors

Figure 4.12   *Continued.*

Lead Auditor Evaluation

9/22/xx

Lead auditor: Mike   Auditor: Jim

Procedure audited: 6.2-01 Human Resources

A) Checklist questions—comments:

Very good! Just address where and how you will get your own samples.

B) Audit

Rating

++ Excellent

+ Above average

A Average

– Below average

– – Needs improvement

Internal requirement: 5+

Criteria	Weight (1–5 scale, 5 = most important)	Name M. G.
Persistence	5	A
Ability to balance big picture with detail	3	–
Written skills	4	+
Verbal skills	2	+
Assertive	2	+
Constructive	1	+
Organized	3	A
Participation during audit	4	+
Leadership role	5	–
Total:		5+

Positive Comments:

Good start—made auditee feel comfortable

Show me the results of fire suppressant training—good

Good paraphrasing—got the auditee to talk more!

Areas for Possible Improvement:

Explain auditor/auditee roles at the beginning

Explain scope better

Don't read questions from standard—understand them and phrase them in your own words

Figure 4.13   Example of an internal auditor evaluation form.

Start off with big-picture questions

Remember, you are auditing a process, not the process owner. Feel free to go audit the other roles in the process

Need to go see samples!!!!

Summarize the end results, possible findings and discuss the closing meeting

"Show me examples of education, training experience". . . and then later, "examples of job descriptions." You need to pull your examples!!!

Follow the auditee—look over his shoulder when he is searching for a record

Hurry the process along if the auditee is taking too much time finding a record

Focus some questions on effectiveness

Persist in seeing records—even if they can not get into a drive—ask if someone else can

Pay attention to recording more notes and perhaps copying some records that were referenced

C) CAPA Evaluation

Criteria	#503	#504	#505	#506	#507	#508
Quality of the requirement recorded	5	5	1	1	5	5
Quality of the evidence recorded	2	2	4	3	3	4
Significance to ISO 9001	4	3	2	2	1	3
Significance to company	3	2	2	2	3	3
Total	14	12	9	8	12	15

(5 = High, 3 = Acceptable, 1 = Needs improvement)

Figure 4.13 *Continued.*

5

Lean ISO 9001 Maturity Assessment Model

LEAN

Of great interest these days is a *lean maturity assessment model*. Companies wish to determine how well they are progressing in their lean journey and oftentimes wish to have an outsider come into their facility to do such an assessment. It is indeed recommended to have an unbiased and consistent assessment done on a periodic basis to monitor progress and help develop further strategy for the upcoming years.

When performing a lean maturity assessment, I recommend using the SAE J4000 standard entitled *Identification and Measurement of Best Practice in Implementation of Lean Operation*. Personally, I like *most* of the questions asked and how they are categorized into the following element numbers:

4. Management/trust

5. People

6. Information

7. Supplier/organization/customer chain

8. Product

9. Process/flow

I also think that the rating scale used to rate each question is useful in discerning progress and maturity when assessments are done periodically:

Level 0: The component is not in place at all or there are major inconsistencies in implementation.

Level 1: The component is in place but there are minor inconsistencies in implementation.

Level 2: The component is fully in place and effectively implemented.

Level 3: The component is fully in place, effectively implemented, and exhibits improvement in execution over the past 12 months.

Since this standard is not something that any one particular company has to comply with (unless required to do so by a customer), I've oftentimes suggested that a company use this standard and the specific questions as a baseline or a foundation and modify it as necessary.

ISO 9001

From an ISO 9001 standpoint, it is recommended to consider using Annex A, Guidelines for self-assessment, in ISO 9004. As it implies, this assessment tool uses ISO 9004 as its basis for monitoring progress, and since ISO 9004 represents the spirit behind ISO 9001, this is a great approach and focus. This checklist also requires the use of a variable scale to assess progress and maturity of an effective and efficient QMS (see Table 5.1).

As in the case of the lean maturity assessment checklist, unless a customer mandates the use of this checklist, an organization can modify the questions asked to suit its needs.

LEAN ISO 9001

If an organization buys into most or all of everything written in this book, wishes to progress toward an effective and efficient lean ISO 9001 system, and would like to have an assessment of not just one system, but the integration and effectiveness of the two systems, then the organization may wish to extract questions from both sources listed above as well as from this book and develop its own specific and unique lean ISO 9001 maturity assessment model.

I oftentimes will add in questions from the great Dr. W. Edward Deming's principles as detailed in his classic book *Out of the Crisis* or in my follow-up book, *Out of Another @#&*% Crisis!* I do this because I am a firm believer in Dr. Deming's huge influence on the development of the Toyota Production System, or what most people today call *lean*.

Table 5.1 ISO 9004 Annex A table of performance maturity levels.

Maturity level	Performance level	Explanation
1	No formal approach	No systematic approach evident, no results, poor results, or unpredictable results.
2	Reactive approach	Problem- or corrective-based systematic approach; minimum data on improvement results available.
3	Stable formal system approach	Systematic, process-based approach, early stage of systematic improvements; data available on conformance to objectives and existence of improvement trends.
4	Continual improvement emphasized	Improvement process in use; good results and sustained improvement trends.
5	Best-in-class performance	Strongly integrated improvement process; best-in-class benchmarked results demonstrated.

For one particular client, I did develop a unique lean ISO 9001 maturity assessment checklist (see Figure 5.1) based on their specific needs and format desired and what I believed was important in an advanced QMS. Most of the focus was on the effectiveness of their QMS, but since this was a company that also had a very active lean program, I convinced them to include lean maturity questions and lean ISO 9001 integration questions. Furthermore, the reader will notice in Figure 5.1 that two of the sections' questions are derived from David Mann's book, *Creating a Lean Culture,* and the SAE J4000 standard referred to above, both of which contain key elements to an effective lean ISO 9001 system

The rating system was not a scaled system based on the clients' requirements, but rather every question was answered as either "yes" or "no." I formatted the questions so that an answer of "yes" to each question was the best answer and so that a total number of yeses or a percentage of yeses could be compared during each review period.

Quality Rating System

1. Effectiveness of the registration system

   a. Does proof exist that ISO 9001 certification has decreased costs through improvements in product/process quality?

   b. Does proof exist that ISO 9001 certification has increased customer satisfaction through improvements in product quality?

   c. Has there been an attempt to document the value of being registered?

   d. As a result of registrar surveillance audits, have any actions been taken above and beyond those that have to be taken (i.e., documented nonconformities)?

   e. Have your requirements for registrar performance been documented and agreed upon with the registrar?

   f. Do you evaluate your registrar's performance?

   g. Have you issued corrective or preventive actions to your registrar?

   h. Do you openly point out weak areas in your processes to the registrar auditor?

   i. Are normal hours worked by all employees just prior to a surveillance audit?

2. Effectiveness of the management review process

   a. Is the management review process viewed as a process that adds value?

   b. Does top management personally initiate corrective and preventive actions resulting from the management review process?

   c. Are management review meetings conducted according to schedule?

   d. Is the effectiveness of the corrective action and internal auditing system viewed as an indicator of the effectiveness of the management review process?

   e. Is the quality management system viewed as a business management system?

3. Effectiveness of objectives

   a. Do the objectives and goals challenge the company to improve?

   b. Are the majority of the objectives and goals being achieved?

   c. In such cases that goals are not being achieved, is there a documented action plan with due dates and defined responsibilities?

Figure 5.1 Lean ISO 9001 maturity assessment checklist.

    d. Is the corrective and preventive action system being used to achieve objectives and goals?

    e. Are the objectives and goals of the QMS integrated with the site's overall objectives and goals, including those of a financial or efficiency nature?

    f. Is there a direct relationship between the objectives of the site and the quality policy and any applicable vision, values, and/or mission statements that exist?

4. Effectiveness of the corrective/preventive action process

    a. Are there incentives or goals to maximize the number of preventive actions?

    b. Are there incentives or goals to maximize the number of corrective actions?

    c. Is the creation and completion of corrective/preventive actions viewed as a value stream?

    d. Are there balanced goals to drive the effectiveness and efficiency of the corrective/preventive action system (i.e., # of corrective/preventive actions resulting in a documentation change and # of corrective/preventive actions completed on time)?

    e. Is there a way to measure/evaluate recurring problems as a means to determine effectiveness of the corrective action system?

    f. Is the corrective action system tied in directly to FMEAs?

    g. Is root cause analysis (i.e., the 5 whys, cause-and-effect diagrams, DOE) tied in directly to the corrective and preventive action system?

    h. Are production workers and team leads taught root cause analysis in a way that it can be performed easily and daily?

    i. Are the 8 process wastes (except for "defects") that are observed within the company initiators of preventive actions?

    j. Is the lean philosophy fully integrated into the corrective/preventive action system so that there is no waste in any continual improvement system?

    k. Is this process believed to be the most important process in the company by the majority of employees?

    l. Is it well understood by top management that lean tools (i.e., 5S, quick changeovers, TPM) are only possible solutions to good root cause analysis, and that there might be other solutions?

Figure 5.1 *Continued.*

m. Is it well understood by top management that the root cause of ineffective corrective/preventive actions and other continual improvement processes (ISO, lean, Six Sigma, etc.) is not ensuring that root cause analysis within the company is effective?

n. Is there a way to measure or evaluate reoccurring problems as a means to determine effectiveness of the corrective action system?

5. Effectiveness of the internal audit system

a. Are internal audits viewed as a good thing for the company by the majority of employees?

b. Do the majority of the process owners want their processes to be audited?

c. Do your internal auditors generate more preventive actions than corrective actions?

d. Have your auditors been trained in lean, non-value-added versus value-added, and the 8 process wastes as a way to audit "effectiveness"?

e. Have your auditors discussed how to enhance the audit program through the review of ISO 19011 and ISO 9004?

f. Do your auditors reject a high percentage of corrective/preventive actions that do not address the root cause of a problem?

g. Do your auditors represent the "cream of the crop" of employees or those who have the most time available?

h. Are your auditors well versed in root cause analysis?

i . Is at least one of your internal auditors a member of top management?

j. Do your internal auditors also audit supplier facilities?

k. Are your internal auditors encouraged to be tough?

l. Is there any incentive to record findings on high-impact issues over low-impact issues?

m. Are auditors recognized for their work?

n. Is there a job description for internal auditors used to identify new auditors based on auditor characteristics (e.g., persistence)

o. Do auditors evaluate the sustainability of lean efforts (e.g., adherence to kanban quantities, TPM, single-piece flow)?

p. Do auditors evaluate the areas that have undergone a 5S transformation on an ongoing basis and drive accountability?

Figure 5.1   *Continued.*

q. Are auditors evaluated on audit techniques (based on defined criteria) as well as the nonconformities they write, for the sake of improvement?

r. Is there an effectiveness of internal auditing evaluation?

s. Is there a system in place to allow for and encourage any employee to request an internal audit?

t. Do auditors determine the effectiveness of the solutions to the nonconformities they personally observed and documented?

6. Effectiveness of determining competency of new hires or employees assigned new roles

    a. Are there job descriptions for value stream managers, management reps, Green Belts, Black Belts, team leaders, and all leaders documented and used to improve the effectiveness of these roles?

    b. Is training effectiveness of the internal auditor training determined, and does it drive changes for future training?

    c. Is training effectiveness of root cause analysis training determined, and does it drive changes for future training?

    d. Is the "hiring of new employees" process focused on hiring problem preventers over problem solvers, and is this evidenced in documented job descriptions?

    e. In most cases, are criteria clearly established when determining whether an individual is competent enough to do his/her work unsupervised?

    f. Has an appropriate amount of quality tools training (i.e., DOE, SPC, FMEA, gage R&R, quality planning) been provided to those who should have it?

    g. For those who have been trained in these quality tools, has there been an effective use of these tools, such that real improvement and controls have been made as a direct result of the use of these tools?

7. Effectiveness of integrating continual improvement tools to drive out CI waste

    a. Has there been a strong effort at integrating applicable CI tools (i.e., MVP group, lean, ISO 9001, Six Sigma, goal deployment process)?

    b. Has there been a substantial effort made to make the quality management system leaner (i.e., applying the principles of 5S to the documentation system to get rid of the waste)?

Figure 5.1 *Continued.*

---

    c. Has there been a substantial effort to reduce the lead time to change a procedure/work instruction?

    d. Are process owners (ISO 9001) and value stream managers (lean) one and the same?

    e. Are lean and Six Sigma processes documented in the quality management system (i.e., a 5S work instruction, tollgate review procedure)?

    f. Are Six Sigma, ISO 9001, goal deployment process, and lean objectives and goals one and the same?

    g. Is it clearly defined in your QMS what the criteria are for doing a lean project versus a Six Sigma project versus a corrective action versus a preventive action?

    h. Do lean projects utilize the corrective and preventive action form, ensuring that root cause is determined prior to making improvements?

    i. Is the overall leader for ISO 9001, lean, and Six Sigma efforts the same person?

    j. Has there been a substantial effort in reducing the number of approvals (reducing lean office waste) of procedures and work instructions to no more than two individuals?

    k. Do QMS auditors or layered process auditors also perform 5S assessments at the same time, when applicable?

8. Effectiveness of lean culture deployment (Source: *Creating a Lean Culture*)

    a. Do leaders have and follow standard work, including review of the standard work followed for each value stream?

    b. Is standard work regularly updated?

    c. Are standard work documents displayed visually?

    d. Is standard work used to smooth transitions between leaders?

    e. Are visual controls in evidence for production processes?

    f. Are visuals current?

    g. Do visuals drive improvement?

    h. Are visual controls in evidence for non-production (support) processes?

    i. Are visuals current?

    j. Do visuals drive improvement?

    k. Do daily meetings focus on process and results?

Figure 5.1   *Continued.*

l. Do startup meetings have a purpose beyond daily production?

m. Are tasks assigned from meetings?

n. Do assignments address interruptions?

o. Are support groups integrated with value stream improvement?

p. Are there documented definitions for all processes?

q. Does documentation match actual practice?

r. Is standard work available for production tasks and does it include takt time?

s. Are operator balance charts available?

t. Are balance charts posted for flow areas?

u. Are items besides production reviewed? (5S, attendance, training)

v. Do crisis situations result in shortcutting the process?

w. Is emphasis placed on reasons why misses occur?

x. Are all applicable leaders conducting gemba walks?

y. Are data used to solve problems?

z. Prior to changes, are problems anticipated before they happen?

aa. Do leaders ask "why?" before jumping to solutions?

bb. Are problem-solving tools used and understood?

cc. Is process improvement cross-functional?

dd. Are line workers involved in improvement activities?

ee. Are assignments made and tracked visually for process improvements?

ff. Are tasks followed through to actual changes in the process?

gg. Is there a method for submitting improvement suggestions?

9. Effectiveness in lean strategy deployment (Source: Management/Trust section of SAE J4000)

a. Is continuous progress in implementing lean operating methods the organization's primary tool in pursuing its strategic objectives?

b. Are structured policy deployment techniques used to plan the organization's lean deployment actions?

c. Are lean progress targets defined and effectively communicated?

d. Has the knowledge of the philosophy and mechanics of lean operation been obtained and effectively communicated?

Figure 5.1 *Continued.*

---

    e. Are the organization's senior managers actively leading the deployment of lean practices?

    f. Is lean progress reviewed by senior management against planned targets on a regular basis?

    g. Are meaningful incentives that reward organizational lean progress in place?

    h. Is individual managers' performance evaluated and rewarded relative to lean progress?

    i. Does a non-blaming, performance-oriented, process-driven organizational atmosphere exist?

    j. Is there a regular, direct personal involvement by senior managers with the operating workforce concerning lean practices?

    k. Is consistent policy for disposition of individuals made superfluous by lean progress in place and followed?

    l. Does no employee have reason to perceive their livelihood to be jeopardized by contributing to organizational lean progress?

    m. Has management chosen to adhere to lean principles in the face of short-term operating objectives inconsistent with lean progress?

10. Miscellaneous

    a. Is the benchmarking of other companies an important strategic element in the improvement of continual improvement efforts?

    b. Are operators intimately aware of the voice of the customer buying the products?

    c. Are operators knowledgeable of all customer satisfaction and dissatisfaction results?

    d. Are significant efforts made to assist in the improvement of supplier processes?

    e. Are operators involved in supplier evaluations?

    f. Is the effectiveness of the gage verification/calibration process measured, and are changes to process/frequency made as a result of the evaluations?

    g. Has there been a substantial effort to incorporate the finance, marketing, and safety departments into the quality management system and lean efforts?

Figure 5.1   *Continued.*

Appendix A
Lean and Quality Terms

A3—The process by which an organization identifies, frames, and then acts on problems and challenges at all levels—perhaps the key to the entire system of developing talent and continually deepening the organization's and individuals' knowledge and capabilities.

corrective (and preventive) action—Action taken to eliminate the cause of a detected (potential) nonconformity or other undesirable (potential) situation.

daily accountability process—A brief process by which a process-oriented team reviews how the team fared in meeting its expected results from the previous day, understand why they did meet certain expectations, and assign actions to eliminate root causes of problems. *See* lean culture.

daily production boards—The most frequently used communication device and visual management tool (*see* lean culture), which shows actual versus expected results throughout the day or shift with explanation recorded by the people doing the work as to why actual results did not meet expected results, when applicable.

effectiveness—Extent to which planned activities are realized and planned results achieved.

efficiency—Relationship between the result achieved and the resources used.

5S—Sort, set in order, shine, standardize, and sustain—a methodology that helps to maintain organizational orderliness, allowing for a smooth and efficient flow of activities and the minimization of operator errors.

gemba walk—Going to the place of action for the purpose of understanding the process, identifying waste, and teaching others how to see the waste. *See* lean culture.

job breakdown sheet—A document that breaks down a job into its major steps, its key points, and the reasons *why* the key points are key points. It is a document that provides the trainer with the format for properly training employees to ensure competency, and it is part of the Job Instruction module of TWI. *See* Chapter 3, G. Integrating TWI with Job Competency Requirements.

kaizen—Continuous improvement; improvements made every day by everybody; the small, gradual, incremental changes applied over a long period of time that add up to a major impact on business results.

kanban—"Card" or "sign." It is the name given to the inventory control card in a pull system. It is also the system of information that integrates the plant, connects all processes to one another, and harmoniously connects the entire value stream to the customer demand.

leader standard work—Typically a working document that defines expectations of those in management positions, ensuring that the standard work is being followed and process improvement is occurring. *See* lean culture.

leadership discipline—The discipline of those in management acting as leaders, such that they are mentoring, teaching, and coaching those who work for them, and not micromanaging them. *See* lean culture.

lean culture—As defined by David Mann, lean culture is made up of the following four principles:[19]

leader standard work—A structure and routine, as defined on a transportable working document, that helps leaders shift from a sole focus on results to a dual focus on process plus results.

visual controls—The premise behind visual controls is that the status of virtually every process should be visible in lean management. The purpose is to allow greater focus on the process and make it easy to compare expected versus actual performance.

daily accountability process—Through the use of daily meetings and visual controls, task assignments, due dates, and resources are determined by the meeting leader for the improvements that will be worked on.

leadership discipline (including gemba walks)—Becoming apprenticed to a sensei (or lean teacher) and the principal method by which a sensei teaches: the gemba walk. Gemba is roughly translated as "the actual place." "Actual" refers to where the action is happening.

nonconformity—Nonfulfillment of a requirement.

OEE (overall equipment effectiveness)—Used in TPM programs (*see*), OEE is an index that clarifies the impact of the six big losses (breakdowns, setups and adjustments, reduced speed, minor stoppages, defects and rework, startup loss) and provides a measure of the overall health of equipment. OEE = availability + performance + quality.

quality at the source—Inspection and product rework are accommodated at any point in a product's life as it is being produced, not at a later point in production by a QC person. It usually involves: source inspection to catch errors before they become defects, 100 percent inspection to check every work piece, not just a sample, immediate feedback to shorten the time for corrective action, and mistake-proofing devices to check automatically for abnormalities.

quality management system (QMS)—Management system to direct and control an organization with regard to quality.

quick changeover (or SMED—single minute exchange of dies)—A theory and set of techniques that make it possible to perform equipment setup and changeover operations in under 10 minutes.

root cause analysis—A class of problem-solving methods aimed at identifying the root causes of problems or events.

standard work combination sheet—A document, normally used by operators, that is used to define the standard work of an operation so that the work can be improved. It normally contains three main elements: takt time (time required to complete one job at the pace of customer demand), the sequence of doing things, and how much inventory or stock on hand the individual worker needs to have in order to accomplish that standard work.

TPM (total productive maintenance)—A team-based productive maintenance that involves every level and every function in the organization, from top executives to the shop floor.

TWI (Training Within Industry)—*See* Appendix F.

value stream manager—The manager whose job it is to understand the entire flow of a product or product group through the company. This person is empowered to maximize the value of the entire system and avoid suboptimization of certain departments and functions.

value stream mapping—A lean technique used to analyze the flow of materials and information currently required to bring a product or service to a consumer.

visual controls—The process and controls used to make the status of every process visible to anyone, even the casual observer walking near the process. *See* lean culture.

Appendix B

Abolish the ISO Registration System, As It Is, Before It's Too Late!

WHO'S RESPONSIBLE FOR IMPROVING THE EFFECTIVENESS OF THE REGISTRATION SYSTEM?

It's broken people, and no one is fixing it!! The grand experiment is not working!

In theory, the third-party audit system was supposed to allow for completely objective audits performed by a company outside of the normal supply chain of conducting business. Ideally, a registrar could provide a completely unbiased audit to an ISO standard and not care if the audited organization is unhappy with the results (that is, a rejected certification, placing a company on "probation") because the audited company represents such a small amount of business to that registrar that the auditors can be completely objective.

Well, it's not working, as documented by these respondents to my Fall 2004 article published in *Quality Management Forum* entitled, "Easy Audits—The Downfall of ISO 9001:2000":

> *Our registrar doesn't give us the value I desire to get from them: the incentive to improve. The rest of my management group thinks we are so good because after every audit there are just some minor, obscure things to fix. The problem I see with the registrar we use (and some of it for sure is the competency of the auditor) is that they really don't look at the bigger picture and actually determine if the processes we are following are*

*actually meeting the intent of the standard and causing
the company to improve.*

—Alan E. Schneidewent, Corporate Quality Director

*A group that conducts assessments of suppliers recently
visited a new supplier who was asking to be qualified
to supply on contracts. Their assessment was that the
company had made an enthusiastic beginning and with
sustained effort should be ISO 9001:2000–compliant
within a year. Two weeks later they received a
successful ISO 9001:2000 registration audit. When
I questioned the lead auditor who said that, "they've
made a good start and we wanted to encourage them
to continue," he fully admitted that they were not fully
compliant and begged me not to make a fuss. Too late—
the customer is already making a fuss!*

*I've had several clients who have dropped their
certification because they see no value and a lot of
aggravation from their registrar auditors.*

—David Jenkins

I received many more responses of a similar nature from all over the
world.

So who will take action? Will ANAB (ANSI–ASQ National Accreditation Board), who receives payments from the registrars to conduct said audits, or the IAF (International Accreditation Forum, www.iaf.nu), of which it is a member? In this there is a conflict of interest. Will the companies who receive certifications, many of whom only care about the receipt and maintenance of said certificate? Will the registrars, who are mostly concerned currently with obtaining surveillance audit business from other registrars and who appear to be primarily concerned with short-term profits rather than meeting the needs of their true customer—the ISO 9001 standard?

Who will step up to take action before the demise of ISO 9001? At this point, it is in no one's best interest to take real action with the exception of those who truly believe and live by the spirit of ISO 9001, those who follow Deming's principles, and those who truly believe that quality of product or service is more important than short-term profit.

In my own experience, I have witnessed the following data from *five different certified* companies:

1. Two internal audit findings and no preventive actions in five years

2. No registrar surveillance audits for 10 years

3. 110 open corrective actions; two closed during the last year

4. No proof of root cause determination (it's not on their corrective action form), no internal audits, no management review for two years

5. An obvious design-responsible company who claimed an exclusion to 7.3, Design and development, and has been allowed to do so for two-plus years

Are these not major nonconformities? Should these companies not be decertified or, at least, be placed on "probation"?

TWO SEPARATE ENTITIES: ISO 9001 AND THE REGISTRATION SYSTEM

ISO 9001: *Good!* Registration system: *Bad!*

These are two separate entities, which, unfortunately, are perceived by many to be one and the same. Because it is so easy to obtain and maintain an ISO 9001 certificate, many people may think that ISO 9001 does not work. It's not the standard that does not work. It is the registration system that does not work because it no longer drives continual improvement efforts.

This linkage is an unfortunate calamity because if top management chooses to live by the spirit of ISO 9001, they would find that it is a great foundation and structure to truly improve business operations and the bottom line.

So what is the root cause of an ineffective registration system? Let's use the five whys to find out:

1. The registration system is ineffective because the registrars perceive that what the client really wants is a certificate and as few nonconformities as possible, so the auditors provide easy audits. *Why?*

2. Registrar auditors perform easy audits because they are directed to do so by their top management. *Why?*

3. Registrar top management directs auditors to perform easy audits in order to maintain whatever business they can and to cease further erosion of the registration business. *Why?*

Examples:

> *I have worked as a contract lead ISO 14001 auditor for two different registrars. One of the two registrars instructed me to spend most of my time on the paper system and got upset when I found too many issues out in the plant (I have stopped working for them). They actually certified a plant that had three major nonconformances, sending another auditor when I refused to pass them in time for the plant to meet an auto industry deadline.*
>
> —Randy Roig

> *I also have had lead assessors tell me they have to be easy on the customers to avoid criticism from their management.*
>
> —Frits Verdonk

4. Registrars perform easy audits because they *can* do whatever they want because the system of checks and balances is ineffective and there is currently no effective manner of evaluating the *effectiveness* of the audits that they provide. *Why?*

5. It is not in anyone's best interest to challenge the system—in the short term.

As we all know, when performing root cause analysis there can be many branches or paths to go down. Starting from the same point, another path could be:

1. The registration system is ineffective because the registrars perceive that what the client really wants is a certificate and as few nonconformities as possible, so the registrars give the client what it wants. *Why?*

2. Registrars perceive this because the client does not tell them what they want from the audit—they just sign the registrar's contract. Clients do not follow 7.4 (Purchasing) of ISO 9001 for purchasing of registration services, so registrars follow 7.2.1.b and determine "requirements not stated by the customer . . . ." *Why?*

3. Clients do not follow 7.4 because they do not want to put in writing that they only want a certificate and they are only doing it to maintain or gain business. *Why?*

4. Client top management does not believe in or does not understand continual improvement. *Why?*

5. Client top management does not understand that increased quality leads to decreased costs and more profits in the long run. They do not understand the spirit of ISO 9001.

THE LEGGETT & PLATT STORY

(Contributions made by Steven W. Willis, Staff VP Quality Systems, Leggett & Platt, Inc.)

Leggett & Platt (L&P) *has* done something about the lack of value they were receiving from initial and surveillance audits conducted by certain registrars.

L&P, a Fortune 500 company, has just over 300 sites worldwide, and at one point had 69 sites certified to an ISO 9001–based quality system. L&P had contracts with 20 different registrars and they were unhappy with the value and variation they were receiving, so L&P decided to take two major actions:

1. Sites *not* mandated to be ISO 9001–certified by a customer would not employ the services of an outside registrar. L&P would develop an internal certification process at the corporate level (ensuring auditor objectivity by not allowing certification audits to be performed by site employees). If these sites passed the audit, they would be termed LP 9000 certified.

2. The remaining sites would be certified by one registrar that would receive the business after L&P performed an in-depth selection and evaluation process of the current registrars.

The short-term results:

1. Seventy-seven sites have been certified to LP 9000, with an additional 30 targeted in the next two years.

2. Significant savings per annum in choosing one supplier of registration services.

3. Because of the leverage they now possess with the remaining registrar, they have met with the top management of the registrar and better defined L&P's expectations of audits: more value-added time spent auditing and more identified corrective and preventive actions. Finding a good registrar and establishing expectations is key to getting the value out of third-party certification for the 69 locations and future sites.

The long-term results: At some point in the future, L&P will perform an evaluation and comparison of effectiveness between ISO 9001 and LP 9000.

WHAT CAN SMALLER COMPANIES DO?

Leggett & Platt is a large company and they can afford to take the above actions because of the number of sites they have. What can other, smaller companies do?

1. Top management needs to obtain training regarding the spirit of ISO 9001 and how it can and should be used as a *business* management system, not a quality management system, and they need to see how an effective QMS will affect profits.

2. Define your requirements to the registrar on the purchase order or other document, including what deliverables you want from the audit and in what format (including perhaps the use of your internal forms).

3. Evaluate the performance of the auditor and the registrar based on your defined criteria and provide that information to them as a means of improvement. It is your supplier!!

4. Issue corrective actions to the registrar when they do not meet your requirements and preventive actions when their performance is ineffective and could lead to a potential issue.

5. Follow Leggett & Platt's lead, if possible, depending on your customers' requirements and the size of the company. Even if your customer(s) require ISO 9001 certification, maybe you can change their minds with a better plan!

6. Top management must also learn that if their company is involved with lean or Six Sigma, that these need to be fully integrated into a company's ISO 9001–based business management system (BMS), as a subset of the BMS, in order to be truly effective.

WHAT SHOULD QUALITY PURISTS DO?

1. Set up a meeting with an ASQ Section, an association, industry group, or a panel of ISO 9001–certified companies to study, discuss, and determine the effectiveness of the ISO 9001 registration business with the goal of developing suggestions to ensure that the integrity of the ISO 9001 principles are upheld and that the ISO God is happy.

2. Complain directly to ANAB by logging on to www.anab.org, and clicking on "Complaints."

3. Develop suggestions for radical change to the system and present them to ANAB, including:

   a. Elimination of the current registration system, as it stands today, and the development of one organization to perform said audits with the same fee structure for all companies. Learn from the weaknesses and strengths of the FDA.

   b. Development of a rating system for ISO 9001–certified companies, complete with criteria, objectives, and goals, and consequences for good/poor performance (for example, Platinum level—1 audit per year, Silver—2 audits per year, Bronze—3 audits per year), rewards and recognition, and criteria/consequences for becoming decertified.

   c. Requirements for registrars to disclose how many companies they put on probation and how many they decertify.

   d. Establish quantitative measures of effectiveness of registrars, performed by a third party, based on client performance.

   e. Come up with other ideas!!

4. Speak up, present papers, write articles, complain to ANAB and/or IAF, complain to your registrar, develop other internal options for auditing or certifying companies to ISO 9001!!

The main thing that we must not let happen is for ISO 9001 to die a slow death. In its current format, ISO 9001 has so much potential to help improve global product quality for the betterment of society. However, due to the ease of gaining and maintaining a certificate, the certificate itself is being devalued and it is being taken down with the registration system ship. It's time to take action before it's too late!

Appendix C
Turtle Diagrams, Registrar Auditors, and More Waste

Over the past several months, three different former or current clients have informed me that it was *strongly recommended* to them that they develop and install *turtle diagrams* for each of their processes. This recommendation did not come from consultants, but rather it came from the registrar auditors. In fact, two auditors from one registrar taught my former client how to develop turtle diagrams by drawing them on the whiteboard, *during a surveillance audit.*

In my stand-up quality comedy routine that I perform for different quality and lean organizations, conferences, and corporate events, I reveal my very sarcastic list of "Seven Basic Habits of Highly Effective Registrar Auditors." Habit #2 is "Inform the auditee that you are not allowed to give advice . . . and then give advice." I then reveal a double-billed cap (Figure C.1), and state that in the spirit of clause 7.5.3, Identification and traceability, of ISO 9001, registrar auditors should be required to identify their service at the time of provision.

So when the auditor is auditing, he should show the "Auditor" side of the cap. But as soon as he starts to give advice, he should be required to flip the cap around and reveal the word "Consultant." (This hat is available for purchase at www.mikemick.com.)

Registrar auditors are *not* supposed to be giving advice because they then lose their objectivity!

Of the three companies that developed the turtle diagrams for their registrar auditors, none of them have found any value in them. They are not used for training employees or in any other capacity within the company. In some cases, they have even confused the employees. They serve no value except to the auditor.

Do not change your quality management system (QMS) for your registrar auditor! Change your QMS only to make your system more effective,

Figure C.1   Double-billed auditor/consultant cap.

and then to ensure that it meets the intent of ISO 9001, not some auditor's interpretation.

WHY DO REGISTRAR AUDITORS STRONGLY SUGGEST THAT YOU DEVELOP TURTLE DIAGRAMS?

Because it makes their job easier . . . . They need to show proof in their records, as part of the process auditing approach, that you have identified inputs, outputs, and objectives of each process, and then they need to record the same. If they can just obtain a copy of your turtle diagram, then their job is a lot easier and there is more time to talk about the weather.

If a registrar auditor asks you to develop turtle diagrams (or any other type of document):

1. Ask them to show you in ISO 9001 where it states that they are required, and then

2. Ask them to show you their turtle diagrams, as examples, of the contract review process used with your company, the auditing process currently being used, the customer complaint process you might use, and the issuance of the certificate process, which you expect to be used in the near future.

DOES ISO 9001 REQUIRE TURTLE DIAGRAMS?

No, it does not. If you read the standard from cover to cover, you will find *no* reference to a turtle diagram anywhere. In fact, the closest the standard comes to anything that might be interpreted as a turtle diagram is in Section 0.2, Process approach, in ISO 9001. It states, "An activity using resources, and managed in order to enable the transformation of inputs into outputs, can be considered as a process. Often the output from one process directly forms the input to the next." This is a great definition! But it does not state that a turtle diagram must be drawn to demonstrate these processes.

In 4.1, the General requirements section of ISO 9001, it states that:

The organization shall

a) *determine the processes needed for the quality management system and their application throughout the organization*

b) *determine the sequence and interaction of these processes*

That's it! This can be done thousands of ways. There is no requirement for a turtle diagram.

WHAT IS A TURTLE DIAGRAM?

Two registrar auditors suggested the turtle diagram format shown in Figure C.2. This is a real example. The typical turtle diagram has inputs and outputs surrounding the process in question. How does this diagram do what the procedure or agenda form does not? It even defeats its own purpose—it is not written in process format. Each section contains a list of internal information under the heading, listed in "batches," in no particular process order. For example, how do the three "Support processes" and the two "Linkages" fit in, and when do they fit in? The document is written in "batch" form rather than process flow.

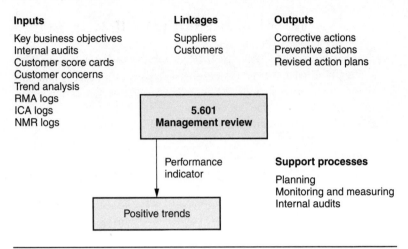

Figure C.2   A real example of a turtle diagram.

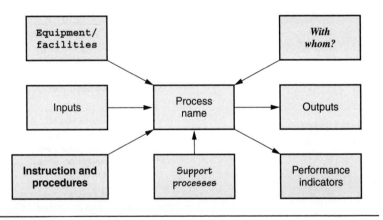

Figure C.3   A typical turtle diagram.

This "turtle diagram" was developed by two registrar auditors for their client during a surveillance audit. It is easy to see how it would be helpful for the auditor and his report, but it is not easy to see how this adds value to the company's quality system.

A more typical turtle diagram is shown in Figure C.3.

WHAT IS A PROCEDURE?

We all know the classical definition. It is a document that explains who does what, when, and where. It is a document that defines a process and cuts across functional or departmental lines (whereas a work instruction is performed by one person or one department).

A well-written procedure will have most of the requirements of a turtle diagram in the body of the document.

Figure C.4 shows an excerpt from a company's process control procedure. Compare the different fonts of the words in this procedure excerpt to the parts of a turtle diagram as shown in Figure C.3.

The "process name" is the title of the document, the "inputs" and "outputs" are obvious when reading how the document flows from one step to the next, and the "performance indicators" can be located in the "Purpose" section of this procedure or in a single objectives and goals form or balanced scorecard organized by process.

Production manager	3. Issues the job to the `specific machine`. Affixes the material identification and traceability sticker on the **traveler**. Makes a copy and gives to *QC*. Sends the original copy to the *shipping and receiving department*. Issues the **setup sheet** to the *setup technician*.
QC	4. Prepares the production folder (consisting of `measuring equipment, including mylars,` when necessary, **in-process sheet, marked-up prints, job instructions, data collection sheet, when necessary, and production gage sheet**).
QC	5. Verifies that the part number and revision level of these documents are accurate when compared to the **traveler**. Searches for any new requirements on the traveler and, if necessary, takes the appropriate action, including the changes to documents in accordance with the *drawing control procedure* (4.2-03).
QC	6. Verifies and calibrates, if necessary, any `gages` that require checking prior to issuance to production, in accordance with the *control of measuring and test equipment procedure* (7.6-01).

Figure C.4 A good example of a procedure format.

SO WHAT'S WRONG WITH TURTLE DIAGRAMS? THEY'RE SLOW!

They are wasteful because they are redundant. They are anti-lean. The information on a turtle diagram should already be in your procedures. You don't need them, and they probably will not be used. They only help the auditor to do his job, and they add complexity to your quality management system.

Most QMSs are way too big and they are growing larger, more complex, and un-user-friendly. Entropy (the law of disorder) has set in, and you have no way to control it. Then your auditor strongly suggests more documents, further complicating your QMS. If the QMS becomes too complex, it will not be used!!

One of my clients, after reading my article on "the Two-Page Quality Manual," hired me to reduce his corporate quality manual. His quality manual was 75 pages in length. He had added a 20-page Six Sigma policy manual and, at the registrar's suggestion, added 27 pages of turtle diagrams. When I stated to the corporate management representative that I bet his 27 turtle diagrams served no value and they were probably not used at all within the company, he admitted that this was correct. He had added them into the system primarily for the auditor. I eventually showed the corporate management rep how to reduce these referenced documents from 122 pages down to five pages through the elimination of redundancies but not any important content. His document is now user-friendly, used, and meets all the requirements of the standard, simply by getting rid of the waste.

Just as a turtle moves slowly, turtle diagrams make your system slower because they add waste to your QMS.

LEAN QUALITY SYSTEMS

You need to ensure that your QMS becomes lean. This does not mean "vague." It means getting rid of the redundancy, of which you have a lot. No requirement, specification, instruction, or procedure should ever be repeated on another document. Having turtle diagrams is redundant with your procedures. I've seen some companies repeat a specification in five or six different places (that is, print, work order, inspection sheet, control plan, work instruction). In this chaotic system, any time a change is made some documents will not be changed. There are too many, and one or more will slip through the cracks and not be changed.

Your obligation as a management representative is to do your job to ensure that your QMS is lean, useful, and user-friendly.

REGISTRAR AUDITORS NEED TO DO THEIR JOB

Regarding my former steady client that received training on how to draw turtle diagrams from the two registrar auditors, I only found out about this after recently providing them with internal auditor training. Five years ago I consulted with them until they were certified. This was my first time back in those five years. Meanwhile, in those five years, this company had not written a single preventive action and had only two internal audit findings—and they were still certified.

Registrars need to do their job and put companies on probation or decertify them if they have major nonconformities. This is their job, and they must be obligated to uphold the spirit of ISO 9001, their true customer. They must stop consulting and advising and start auditing correctly and ensuring that companies are truly qualified to claim ISO 9001 certification.

IT'S YOUR RESPONSIBILITY TO USE THE PRINCIPLES OF LEAN ON YOUR DOCUMENTATION SYSTEM

In effect, some registrars' auditors encourage excessive non-value-added documentation with their advice. Most auditors have had little or no training in lean and elimination of waste. Anything, or anyone, that encourages wasteful activities or wasteful things (such as turtle diagrams, a 50-page quality manual, and *many more examples*) is only encouraging the movement toward ineffectiveness.

Many of you have allowed entropy into your quality system by just blindly accepting whatever the auditor has suggested. Remember that for any nonconformity written or "piece of advice" given, the auditor has to quote a requirement that is not being met. Simply ask the auditor to show you where in the standard turtle diagrams are required and/or where in the standard a lengthy quality manual that mimics the standard is required. This, of course, applies to many other examples.

It is your responsibility to ensure an effective system. Effectiveness is only possible when the system is easy to use. Look for the waste. Look for the inefficiencies and the ineffectiveness within your system. Teach your internal auditors about lean, value added, value stream management, waste elimination, 5S, and/or quick changeover, so that they can help you to do the same.

Appendix D

The Two-Page
Quality Manual

(Note: document control features omitted)

Founded in 1966, Val-Matic is a leading manufacturer of butterfly, plug, air, and check valves for municipal, commercial building, and industrial applications. Val-Matic's corporate offices and manufacturing facilities are located in the Chicago suburb of Elmhurst, Illinois.

Val-Matic's quality management system (QMS) is intended to fully comply with ISO 9001:2000 (no exclusions).

The scope of our quality management system, as recorded on our ISO 9001:2000 certificate is:

The design, development, manufacture, and servicing of water and wastewater valves for municipal and industrial applications

This quality manual represents the scope of Val-Matic's QMS, references the procedures established, identifies the relationships between the procedures and processes established, and defines the interaction between these processes. The relationship between ISO 9001:2000 and Val-Matic's QMS is defined in this quality manual and the internal audit schedule (#).

Val-Matic is committed to live by the spirit of all applicable clauses of ISO 9001, including the requirement to continually improve the effectiveness of its QMS. This commitment is supported by Val-Matic's quality policy statement:

Quality Policy Statement

We are committed to consistently exceeding customer expectations by providing products, services, and information of the highest quality in terms of safety, reliability, accuracy, and timeliness. Our success is based on continuously improving the effectiveness of our products, processes, and quality management system.

This quality policy statement is supported by our documented objectives and goals found in the annually revised objectives and goals form (#).

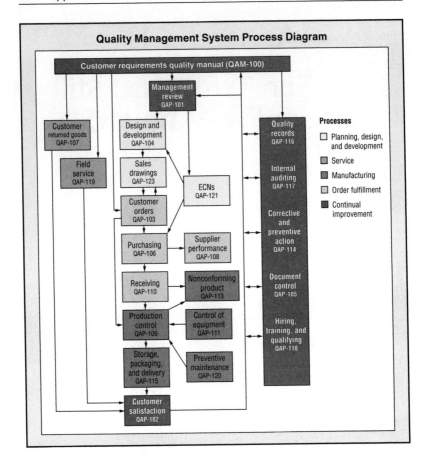

Quality Management System Process Diagram

Explanation of Relationship between Processes, Procedures, and ISO 9001

The titles in the boxes of the flowchart above are the actual procedure titles. If using document numbers, these can be inserted into the boxes as well. If using document numbers, it's best to link the numbering system to the ISO standard (for example, the purchasing procedure could be numbered 7.4-01). Each box can be hyperlinked to the procedure itself.

The company in this example defined each process area by color. These processes define the scope of each internal audit, and have defined objectives and goals that are measured and monitored.

The color coding of these processes could define the relationships to the ISO 9001 standard. This should be done somewhere. This company showed the relationship between each process and the ISO standard in the internal audit schedule.

Appendix E

Ten Signs Your CEO Still Has No Idea About ISO 9001 (and Maybe Lean)

I t's pretty obvious that in so many companies, the CEO and other top managers just do not get ISO 9001 and all the derivative standards, based on their actions and behaviors. These 10 signs are written in no particular order. You need to be the judge within your own organization as to which ones are most prevalent. How many can you relate to?

1. *Congratulates all employees and the management rep for a job well done after receiving only one or two minor nonconformities from the registrar auditor.* The message sent to everyone? "We know we've got a lot more problems than that! We got away with it again. Don't change this auditor. I like him. Great job hiding the problems we really do have! Keep up the good work and make sure you hide more problems in the future, even if you have to work more hours before the audit cleaning up the way we really operate. Make sure we never get a lot of nonconformities—that'll be bad for you! I'm not trying to create fear; I'm just trying to be realistic."

2. *Bases a good portion or any portion of the management rep's performance appraisal on how many nonconformities are received during an audit.* This further exacerbates the above problem. The message sent? "Do not ask for a tough audit from the registrar. Do not ask her to delve into areas you know are weak and need improvement—she will write up more nonconformities—and your pay will be lower. Lead her into the areas where we are strong and away from the weak areas, or people. Also, don't do anything to truly challenge or change the quality management system (QMS). Work within the QMS because it does not give us many nonconformities. What's important is as few nonconformities as possible, not improvement."

3. *Batch processes management reviews.* Most companies hold management review meetings on a monthly, quarterly, semiannual, or even

annual frequency. The message sent? "Even though we are a lean company, those ideas only apply to lean 'stuff' or 'things.' They do not apply to a QMS. A QMS, by nature, is not lean. Things like internal audits and management reviews are done in batches. I mean, think about it. It's easier for me to remember all of the customer feedback, audit results, problems, and opportunities for improvement throughout the year and store all of these thoughts in my big expansive brain full of inventory space, and then blurt it all out once a year, in one big lump. The auditors will love it, because all of the management review requirements will be met and stored in one big ol' record that will be easier for the external auditor to audit. That's what's important—making the auditor's job easier, not reviewing the effectiveness of the QMS more effectively. If we reviewed our system in single-piece flow, a little every day, and made improvements every day, and reviewed other things less frequently in other meetings, the auditor would not like it. Besides, I don't like reviewing our system—once a year is plenty."

4. *Never completes a corrective or preventive action.* The message sent? "Identifying actual and potential problems is beneath me. That's for the workers to do because, after all, they're closest to the problem and they cause most of the problems. It's easier for me to tell others to do root cause analysis because, quite frankly, I don't get it and I don't want to get it. I know that Deming guy said something like 94 percent of all problems are related to the bad system, which is controlled by me. But who listens to him anymore? He must have been wrong. The employees make the mistakes, so the employees must fix them. Now that's empowerment. Yeah, empowerment, that's it, that's what I meant to say at the beginning of my answer. I don't involve myself in the corrective/preventive action system because I want my people to feel empowered. I like that word."

5. *A QMS pertains to quality only.* The message sent? "Don't you dare even think about involving our marketing, sales, strategic, or financial processes in the QMS if we don't have to. Why would we subject those processes to an audit and possible improvement? This is a 'quality' thing, that's what the 'Q' stands for, doofus. It's for the quality department to mainly handle . . . and . . . oh yeah . . . the shop guys too . . . and just a little bit of customer service . . . engineering . . . purchasing . . . but just a little. But it's mainly quality . . . and some shop people. And don't be trying to convince me again that the word 'quality' in 'QMS' is supposed to be an adjective or adverb or one of those things that describes a *business* management system. That's why they didn't call it a BMS. Yeah, your BMS idea is a lot of BS."

6. *Our CAPA and IQA systems stink because that training we had was bad* (CAPA = corrective action/preventive action, IQA = internal quality audit). The message sent? "We never really got it. That CAPA and IQA trainer we had 10 years ago was boring and did not engage our people. Our people are different than most—they need to see real examples in the plant or office. That trainer—he wasn't like that. It doesn't matter that me, the top dude in the company, sat through our annual management review and never saw customer complaints improve. I was just supposed to review the data. The ineffectiveness of our CAPA and IQA systems has nothing to do with the ineffectiveness of our management review system—it was that damn trainer. We're top managers; we don't know how to fix these things. We've never been self-reliant. What can we throw our money at now to improve CAPA? I know—how about that Six Sigma thing."

7. *ISO 9001 doesn't work.* The message sent? "Well maybe I'm wrong. That little piece of paper, that certificate, got us some good business at the beginning. But it didn't really change us, or the way we operate. We've been operating pretty much the same way for 50 years, and we must be good to stay in business that long. OK, the bailout helped too. But ISO, it didn't really do anything for us besides get us a few clients early on. It didn't help our profits, not that a quality thing would ever affect profits. So now I stay out of it. We did it right. I mean, I know those registrar auditors have to perform a very tough audit. I think they're controlled by the FDA. They must be giving us the best audit possible and they can't have any ulterior motive in passing us each audit. So if they're doing a great job and our profits have been stagnant, ISO must not work. It can't be our processes that are broken; it's ISO. But we should keep it anyway because we might need it to get new business from a naive customer that thinks we're good because we have a certificate."

8. *ISO 9001 and lean are separate things.* The message sent? "Have the QMS run by a quality person and have lean run by an operations person. Keep them separate. Keep up the internal competition that we've had for years. I like the internal competition! It brings fire to my organization. Let them duke it out for resources and attention! That's one way to spice up that damned management review meeting. But the lean guy doesn't attend that quality meeting thing. I'll make him go, even though it has nothing to do with him, because I'm the CEO. Anyway, quality is about quality stuff— you know—meeting those specs. And lean is about housekeeping, value streams, kaizen, and a bunch of other Japanese words I can never remember. Lean has nothing to do with quality, except for maybe that one waste that no one ever pays attention to anyway—defects."

9. *Believes that the main way of ensuring competency is through performance evaluations.* The message sent? "Even though I know that most everyone hates the annual performance appraisal, it's a great way to kill two birds with one stone: the people and the ISO requirement. Also, just like with internal audits and the management review meeting, I can do them all in a big batch at the end of the year so I don't have to deal with all the whining throughout the year. That stuff will drive you crazy. Besides, performance reviews are efficient! I can rate the employees against each other, creating even greater competition, I can rate them against performance objectives that they have no control over or hope of ever attaining, I can give both negative and positive (but mostly negative) feedback as a motivator for improvement and as a record for determining competency, I can use the information as means to promote or can them, and I can make them sign it, and stick it in their personnel file until five years after their death in accordance with the control of records procedure. I am exerting my control over these imbeciles and I am ISO 9001 compliant."

10. *Suck up to the registrar auditor.* The message sent? "Even though the registrar auditor is a supplier, let's suck up to her because nonconformities are *really, really* bad and I don't want any. How do we suck up to her? Hmmmm . . . I know, we'll sign her contract and we won't determine our own needs. We'll just do whatever she states on the contract and we'll accept all of her terms. How else can we suck up? Hmmm . . . I know, when they screw up on their billing, on the audit dates, on the type of audit, on the accuracy of the report or contract, on the lack of returned phone calls, or on their rudeness, we won't issue a CAPA or evaluate their performance like we do all of our other suppliers. Can you imagine, if we gave them a CAPA, which is a *really, really* bad thing, they would give us more, and that would really be bad. How else can we suck up? Hmmmm . . . I know, we can ask her questions about herself and her interests and we can encourage her to talk for hours about non-audit-related stuff. She'll feel great because everyone likes talking about themselves, and she won't have time to do what we're paying her to do, and we'll have fewer CAPAs. Everyone wins, and life is great. Oh yeah, and we'll even laugh out loud over her jokes, even the really dumb ones."

How many of these signs can you relate to? What can be done? Even though you've been certified for a long time, education regarding the spirit and principles behind ISO 9001 and lean is so important! But "they" need to start seeing the light.

Appendix F

Why Did TWI Die in the United States in the Late '40s, and Will It Happen Again?

Be flexible in style, but unwavering, like a rock, in principles.

—Thomas Jefferson

Training Within Industry (TWI) could easily die within your company, if your company structure, systems, and practices are not based on principles that will support and sustain the principles behind TWI.

It's time to evaluate and question your company's principles before another good tool comes and goes. So why did TWI go away the first time?

TWI WAS BORN OUT OF A CRISIS

The U.S. government created the TWI Service in August of 1940 as a means of supplying the Allied Powers with the arsenal to defeat Hitler's forces. At this time, the United States was just exiting from the Great Depression. Unemployment was still high, and production capability was low. Supervisors and lead men were in short supply because they were enlisting or being drafted into the military. The world was in a crisis, and yet most Americans did not want the United States to enter into the war because of its own weaknesses.

The purpose of TWI was to increase productivity and allow the United States to become, as Franklin Roosevelt referred to it, the "arsenal of democracy." This, he thought, would win the war without having to enter the war. Of course, we did enter the war, and by 1942 approximately 6000 new workers were entering the U.S. workforce every day to supply this required arsenal for all the Allied forces, including those of the United States.[20]

9 pages remaining *(96.2% read)*

In 1945, the crisis was over. The United States had the strongest and largest production facilities in the world. The U.S. government disbanded the TWI Service when the war ended.

The companies themselves had no incentive to keep to the ideals and practices of TWI, or at least they *saw* no incentive. After all, TWI was developed out of a crisis, not for internal reasons. TWI was not part of the company's makeup. It was not based on the *company's* principles and culture, rather it was based on TWI Service's principles—and the TWI Service was now disbanded. If companies had adopted the principles and culture on which TWI was based for their own sake, for the sake of their own profitability and long-term survival, then perhaps TWI would have survived within these organizations and would have existed to the present day without having to be reborn again as it currently is.

TWI MOVES TO THE NEXT CRISIS

The United States had exited from a crisis in 1945 and was at the top. Japan had exited World War II at the bottom. *Japan* was now in a state of crisis. Several members of General MacArthur's staff were intimately aware of the benefits of TWI and thought it would be beneficial to teach it to Japanese industry. However, they were not just interested in teaching the *tools* of TWI, but also the democratic *principles* behind TWI, such as "Treat people as individuals." There was an ulterior motive to what General MacArthur wished to do. By helping the Japanese become more productive and improve their economy, he could also teach the *principles* of TWI and thus reestablish Japan as a democratic nation.

YOUR COMPANY'S PRINCIPLES AND PRACTICES VERSUS TWI'S PRINCIPLES AND PRACTICES

So what are your company's principles? Many companies have not determined their own principles, and yet this action should have been done first, a long time ago.

My motto is:

Principles first, culture second, practices third, tools fourth!

Ideally, prior to learning the tools of lean, Six Sigma, ISO 9001, or TWI, a company should have determined its principles, established its culture, ensured that its business practices support both, and then developed its own tools or found the tools that support all of the above.

If your company has already established its principles, do your company's practices support its principles? Are your principles and practices aligned with the principles and practices of TWI? If not, TWI will die another death, at least at your company, in answer to the question in the title of this article.

So what are your company's principles? That is up to your company to determine. I've always said that if you copy anything from Toyota, copy its principles, and then develop your own culture, practices, and tools (or style, as Thomas Jefferson referred to in the above quotation).

Your company could copy Toyota's 14 principles, as were so eloquently laid out in Jeffrey Liker's book entitled *The Toyota Way.*

Or, your company could copy the 14 principles of Dr. Deming, as were so descriptively defined in his 1982 blockbuster book, *Out of the Crisis.* After all, so much of what Toyota learned was from Dr. Deming.

When determining your company's principles, it is important to understand that "principles" are fundamentally accepted rules of action or conduct that are generally inarguable depending on one's purpose or goal, such as raising a family, playing a sport, or building a business.

Dr. Stephen Covey, in his landmark book *The 7 Habits of Highly Effective People* wrote:

> *Principles are guidelines for human conduct that are proven to have enduring, permanent value. They're fundamental. They're essentially unarguable because they are self-evident. One way to quickly grasp the self-evident nature of principles is to simply consider the absurdity of attempting to live an effective life based on their opposites. I doubt that anyone would seriously consider unfairness, deceit, baseness, uselessness, mediocrity, or degeneration to be a solid foundation for lasting happiness and success.* [21]

There are many practices that one lives by that are in violation of principles. Hitler was a prime example of this. Practices in the business world can be in direct violation of good business principles.

Many of the *practices* of Six Sigma management are directly in conflict with the principles of both lean and Dr. Deming. Examples include:

1. Having specialized Belt People resolve everyone's problems rather than everyone being involved in problem resolution and continuous improvement.

2. Setting goals of a) dollar savings, b) number of trained Black Belts, or c) number of SS projects completed, rather than focusing on the process. The goal becomes the focus and not the improvement.

3. Focus on projects (continual improvement) versus everyday improvements (continuous improvement).

4. Achievement of 3.4 defects per million opportunities, which has little to do with improvement.

5. Training in batches and wasteful training (using only a very small percentage of what is taught).

6. The Belt becoming the goal, not the knowledge.

All of these inconsistencies between principles and practices lead to an oxymoronic term: Lean Six Sigma, and there have been plenty of morons who have bought into this. On the other hand, the principles of lean and Dr. Deming are aligned with each other.

Once you've determined your company's principles, then, as Thomas Jefferson said:

Be flexible in style, but unwavering, like a rock, in principles.

Stick to your principles, but be flexible in style, or tools. Ensure that all company practices and tools support these principles.

WHAT ARE THE PRINCIPLES BEHIND TWI?

If your company has already received some TWI training, this really should be an exercise to do with your people. It should be for your company to research and determine. It requires thought, and it is a great time to reflect (hansei) on what is being taught and why.

The following principles from other sources may give you some ideas as to what you and your company might determine are the principles behind TWI.

1. The two pillars (principles) of the Toyota Production System:

   Pillar 1: The respect for and involvement of all people

   Pillar 2: The constant focus on the elimination of waste

2. *Toyota Way* principles that are also TWI principles:

Principle 5: Build a culture of stopping to fix problems, to get quality right the first time.

Principle 6: Standardized tasks are the foundation for continuous improvement and employee empowerment.

Principle 9: Grow leaders who thoroughly understand the work, live the philosophy, and teach it to others.

Principle 10: Develop exceptional people and teams who follow your company's philosophy.

Principle 12: Go and see for yourself to thoroughly understand the situation (genchi genbutsu).

Principle 14: Become a learning organization through relentless reflection (hansei) and continuous improvement (kaizen).

3. Deming Points (principles) that are also TWI principles:

Point 5: Improve constantly and forever the system of production and service, to improve quality and productivity, and thus constantly decrease costs.

Point 6: Institute training on the job.

Point 7: Institute leadership. The aim of supervision should be to help people and machines and gadgets to do a better job.

Point 11a: Eliminate work standards (quotas) on the factory floor. Substitute leadership.

Point 12a: Remove barriers that rob the hourly worker of his right to pride of workmanship.

Point 13: Institute a vigorous program of education and self-improvement.

INTERNAL PRACTICES, PERHAPS WITHIN YOUR COMPANY, THAT MAY NOT SUPPORT TWI

The benefits of TWI and lean itself and all of its tools (that is, 5S, value stream management, quick changeover, work cells, TPM, *and* TWI) will never be sustained within an organization unless the company adopts the principles, culture, and supporting practices behind lean. Principles, such as "respect for and involvement of all of the people" and "process focus rather than department/objective/goal focus," need to be in place.

In other words, if a *culture* of blame exists, and the *practices* of employees being chastised, written up, or evaluated poorly because of defects "they" caused are in effect, then lean improvements and TWI benefits will not be sustained because the culture and practices do not support the *principle* of respect for the people.

Or, if a departmentally focused *culture* exists and the *practices* of establishing departmental objectives and rewarding departments for meeting their own goals is are place, then lean improvements and TWI benefits will not be sustained because the culture and practices do not support the *principle* of process focus.

If your company has started down the path of TWI, it may die once again, within your company, if the following practices are in place. These practices are symptoms of principles and a culture that are not aligned with the principles of TWI:

1. Performance evaluations

2. Employees being chastised, written up, or dinged for defective product ("operator error" causes)

3. Departmental objectives, organization, and focus

4. Hiding problems (from auditors and management)

5. Problem solving by Green and Black Belts, not by the people

6. Egotistic management

7. Supervisors at all levels managing by numbers rather than being "at" the process

8. No monitoring/watching of TWI training—no feedback on the process

9. Micromanagement style versus leadership

10. Hiring kids out of college to be production supervisors

11. Supervisors not working the job for an extended period of time before training others

12. No TWI or any training during the last week of the month or year due to an order from above to ship as much as possible (short-term thinking)

13. Mass inspection by another department (QC)

14. Buying materials, components, gages, tools, or equipment from the lowest bidder, regardless of quality and *total* cost

15. *Continual* improvement activities (that is, once-a-month kaizen events/blitzes) rather than *continuous* improvement activities (that is, every day, by everybody)

16. Supervisors not ensuring standard work is being completed

17. Layoffs

18. Excluding certain people from improvement activities

19. Production quotas

20. No preventive maintenance of equipment, and so on

21. No allocation of training resources or time

WHAT TO DO?

1. Have an outsider assess your organization on its principles, culture, and practices to determine its strengths and weaknesses in supporting TWI and lean principles and practices. Report results.

2. Determine your company's principles and proclaim them.

3. Develop/modify the culture and practices to support the principles.

4. Ensure that the tools used now, or in the future, support and are aligned with the principles.

5. "Be flexible in style, but unwavering, like a rock, in principles."

ONE LAST THING—*YOU* COULD HAVE DEVELOPED TWI

How many times on a corrective action report have you seen the "root cause" of the problem being "poor training"? Normally, the action taken as a result of this "root cause" is "retraining," which of course does nothing for the long term, and the problem reoccurs. Why? Because the system did not change! Essentially, a person was blamed again—the trainer. The action is to have the trainer train again, probably the exact same way she or he did before.

If a company had performed a good root cause analysis in the first place and kept asking why the training program was ineffective, it might have found out that some of the root causes may have been:

- No allocation of training resources and time because it's not important.
- Trainers not knowing how to train because there is no system.
- Trainers do not see trainees do the job effectively.
- Work instruction format is too complex.
- Many trainees are learning disabled, dyslexic, or speak another language, and the written and verbal words are not enough to help them understand.
- There is no training plan.
- There is no follow-up plan.
- Trainers are not held accountable for their training actions.
- Trainers are not given feedback.
- Trainers only show how to do something once.
- Trainees do not understand the importance of each major action because it is not recorded anywhere on the work instruction.

TWI's Job Instruction module addresses all of these root causes, and does not blame the trainer or trainee.

Two very important points result from this section:

1. If your company had done root cause analysis well, you could have developed your own TWI process and called it whatever you wanted to call it.

2. "Getting to the root causes of problems" is perhaps the most important principle of all!!

Endnotes

1. Stephen R. Covey, *The 7 Habits of Highly Effective People* (New York: Simon and Schuster, 1989).
2. Jeffrey Liker, *The Toyota Way* (New York: McGraw-Hill, 2003).
3. Ibid.
4. Ibid.
5. "Layered Process Audits . . . Don't Believe They're Just Audits." *Automotive Excellence* (Fall 2005).
6. Dan Jones and Jim Womack, *Lean Thinking: Banish Waste and Create Wealth in Your Corporation* (New York: Simon & Schuster, 1996).
7. John Shook, *Managing to Learn: Using the A3 Management Process to Solve Problems, Gain Agreement, Mentor, and Lead.* (Cambridge, MA: Lean Enterprise Institute, 2008).
8. David Mann, *Creating a Lean Culture: Tools to Sustain Lean Conversions* (New York: Productivity Press, 2005).
9. Donald Dinero, *Training Within Industry: The Foundation of Lean,* (New York: Productivity Press, 2005).
10. Patrick Graupp, "Don't Swap JI Breakdown Sheets and SOPs," TWI News (July 2009). Available at: http://www.twinews.com/issues/2009_07/Dont_Swap_JI_Breakdown_Sheets_and_SOPs.asp. Accessed March 3, 2010.
11. Shigeo Shingo and Productivity Press Development Team, *Quick Changeover for Operators: The SMED System* (New York: Productivity Press, 1996).
12. Mann, *Creating a Lean Culture.*
13. Daniel Markovitz, "5S Isn't Just for Hammers," Evolving Excellence blog (Posted May 9, 2007). Available at: http://www.evolvingexcellence.com/blog/2007/05/5s_isnt_just_fo.html. Accessed February 24, 2010.
14. Daniel Markovitz, "The Paper Chase," *The New York Enterprise Report* (January 4, 2006).
15. Lisa Belkin, "Time Wasted? Perhaps It's Well Spent," *New York Times* (May 31, 2007).

16. Markovitz, "5S."
17. Ibid.
18. Markovitz, "The Paper Chase."
19. Mann, *Creating a Lean Culture.*
20. Dinero, *Training Within Industry.*
21. Covey, *7 Habits.*

Index

J

Japan, adoption of Training Within
    Industry, 132, 226
Jefferson, Thomas, 228
Jenkins, David, 204
job breakdown sheets (JBS), 84,
    132–35
    example, *133*
job competency requirements,
    integrating TWI with, 128–37
Jones, Dan, 116

K

kaizen event (kaizen blitz), versus
    preventive actions, 24, 37, 128

L

lean
    auditing for, 98–112
    and auditors, 98
    definition, 19
    integrating with management
        review, 124–28
    integrating with quality planning,
        116–22
    and ISO 9001, complementary
        nature of, 19–41
    ISO 9001 QMS as "bookends" of,
        19–25
    lack of integration with ISO 9001,
        reasons for, 41–42
    maturity assessment model,
        189–90
    newness of, 25–26
    and preventive actions, 112–15
    principles behind, 27–31
    redundancy with ISO 9001 quality
        management system, 25
    terms (Appendix A), 199
    weaknesses of, how ISO 9001
        compensates for, 40–41
lean culture
    developing, 38

    principles in, 126, 154
    relationship to management
        review, 169–73
lean ISO 9001
    maturity assessment model,
        189–91
    checklist, *192*
    as oxymoron, 13
lean organization, principles behind,
    29–31
lean practices
    integrating with the quality
        management system,
        87–137
    other documents addressing,
        91–98
    work instructions addressing,
        87–91
lean quality management system,
    sustaining, 85
lean quality management systems, 216
Lean Six Sigma, as oxymoron, 13–14,
    228
Learning to See, 87
Leggett & Platt, Inc., 207–8
Liker, Jeffrey, 29, 31, 32, 227

M

management, system approach to,
    lean principle, 30
management review
    integrating lean with, 124–28
    meeting minutes, 173–74
    minimizing waste in, 166–74
    process, determining effectiveness
        of, 168
    relationship to lean culture, 169–73
Managing to Learn, 122
Mann, David, 38, 154, 191, 200
Markovitz, Dan, 164
master lists, of forms and records,
    165–66
meeting minutes, management review,
    173–74
meetings, minimizing, 168–69
Microsoft Office products, 84

R

About QualityQuest, Inc.

Arlington Heights, IL
mike@mikemick.com
www.mikemick.com
847-401-0442

Mike Micklewright started QualityQuest, Inc. in the summer of 1994. Mike is primarily focused on the integration of *lean* and *quality*, because as he frequently states, "Lean and quality really are the same thing." Mike also focuses on helping company executives understand the importance of having the right principles in place to support any and all continuous improvement activities, whether called lean, quality, or whatever may be the next movement. No improvement activities of any sort will have sustained success without the right principles and the culture and business practices to support those principles.

Contact Mike to help support your business improvement activities and/or to provide a keynote presentation for your company, organization, association, and/or conference.

Mike customizes many of his presentations to meet the specific needs of the customer. Some of the services offered include:

Leaning Out Your Company's QMS Documentation

Assessing Your Organization against Deming's, Leadership and/or Lean Principles

Leadership

Deming's Principles in Practice

Root Cause Analysis

The Relationship between Lean and Root Cause Analysis

Creating a Lean Culture

Internal Auditing

Advanced Internal Auditing

Putting Your Internal Audit System on Steroids

Design of Experiments

Failure Mode and Effects Analysis

ISO 9001, ISO/TS 16949, AS 9100, ISO 13485 QMS Establishment

Value Stream Mapping Events

5S, TPM, Kaizen, Quick Changeover

Quick and Easy Kaizen

Mike is a Senior Member of American Society for Quality (ASQ), a Midwest board member of the Association of Manufacturing Excellence (AME), and a member of U.S. TAG to ISO/TC 176. Mike owns a General Engineering degree from the University of Illinois and holds certifications as a Six Sigma Black Belt, Quality Auditor, Quality Engineer, Manager of Quality/Operational Excellence, and Supply Chain Analyst.

Mike has written, produced, and acted in several training videos, including *The ISO Auditors Are Coming, Auditing Nuts and Bolts,* and *Batchin!.* He also provides presentations in which he impersonates Dr. W. Edwards Deming and demonstrates how far removed from his principles we have become.

Belong to the Quality Community!

Established in 1946, ASQ is a global community of quality experts in all fields and industries. ASQ is dedicated to the promotion and advancement of quality tools, principles, and practices in the workplace and in the community.

The Society also serves as an advocate for quality. Its members have informed and advised the U.S. Congress, government agencies, state legislatures, and other groups and individuals worldwide on quality-related topics.

Vision

By making quality a global priority, an organizational imperative, and a personal ethic, ASQ becomes the community of choice for everyone who seeks quality technology, concepts, or tools to improve themselves and their world.

ASQ is...

- More than 90,000 individuals and 700 companies in more than 100 countries

- The world's largest organization dedicated to promoting quality

- A community of professionals striving to bring quality to their work and their lives

- The administrator of the Malcolm Baldrige National Quality Award

- A supporter of quality in all sectors including manufacturing, service, healthcare, government, and education

- YOU

Visit www.asq.org for more information.

ASQ Membership

Research shows that people who join associations experience increased job satisfaction, earn more, and are generally happier*. ASQ membership can help you achieve this while providing the tools you need to be successful in your industry and to distinguish yourself from your competition. So why wouldn't you want to be a part of ASQ?

Networking

Have the opportunity to meet, communicate, and collaborate with your peers within the quality community through conferences and local ASQ section meetings, ASQ forums or divisions, ASQ Communities of Quality discussion boards, and more.

Professional Development

Access a wide variety of professional development tools such as books, training, and certifications at a discounted price. Also, ASQ certifications and the ASQ Career Center help enhance your quality knowledge and take your career to the next level.

Solutions

Find answers to all your quality problems, big and small, with ASQ's Knowledge Center, mentoring program, various e-newsletters, *Quality Progress* magazine, and industry-specific products.

Access to Information

Learn classic and current quality principles and theories in ASQ's Quality Information Center (QIC), *ASQ Weekly* e-newsletter, and product offerings.

Advocacy Programs

ASQ helps create a better community, government, and world through initiatives that include social responsibility, Washington advocacy, and Community Good Works.

Visit www.asq.org/membership for more information on ASQ membership.

*2008, The William E. Smith Institute for Association Research

ASQ Certification

ASQ certification is formal recognition by ASQ that an individual has demonstrated a proficiency within, and comprehension of, a specified body of knowledge at a point in time. Nearly 150,000 certifications have been issued. ASQ has members in more than 100 countries, in all industries, and in all cultures. ASQ certification is internationally accepted and recognized.

Benefits to the Individual
- New skills gained and proficiency upgraded
- Investment in your career
- Mark of technical excellence
- Assurance that you are current with emerging technologies
- Discriminator in the marketplace
- Certified professionals earn more than their uncertified counterparts
- Certification is endorsed by more than 125 companies

Benefits to the Organization
- Investment in the company's future
- Certified individuals can perfect and share new techniques in the workplace
- Certified staff are knowledgeable and able to assure product and service quality

Quality is a global concept. It spans borders, cultures, and languages. No matter what country your customers live in or what language they speak, they demand quality products and services. You and your organization also benefit from quality tools and practices. Acquire the knowledge to position yourself and your organization ahead of your competition.

Certifications Include
- Biomedical Auditor – CBA
- Calibration Technician – CCT
- HACCP Auditor – CHA
- Pharmaceutical GMP Professional – CPGP
- Quality Inspector – CQI
- Quality Auditor – CQA
- Quality Engineer – CQE
- Quality Improvement Associate – CQIA
- Quality Technician – CQT
- Quality Process Analyst – CQPA
- Reliability Engineer – CRE
- Six Sigma Black Belt – CSSBB
- Six Sigma Green Belt – CSSGB
- Software Quality Engineer – CSQE
- Manager of Quality/Organizational Excellence – CMQ/OE

Visit www.asq.org/certification to apply today!

ASQ Training

Classroom-based Training

ASQ offers training in a traditional classroom setting on a variety of topics. Our instructors are quality experts and lead courses that range from one day to four weeks, in several different cities. Classroom-based training is designed to improve quality and your organization's bottom line. Benefit from quality experts; from comprehensive, cutting-edge information; and from peers eager to share their experiences.

Web-based Training

Virtual Courses

ASQ's virtual courses provide the same expert instructors, course materials, interaction with other students, and ability to earn CEUs and RUs as our classroom-based training, without the hassle and expenses of travel. Learn in the comfort of your own home or workplace. All you need is a computer with Internet access and a telephone.

Self-paced Online Programs

These online programs allow you to work at your own pace while obtaining the quality knowledge you need. Access them whenever it is convenient for you, accommodating your schedule.

Some Training Topics Include
- Auditing
- Basic Quality
- Engineering
- Education
- Healthcare
- Government
- Food Safety
- ISO
- Leadership
- Lean
- Quality Management
- Reliability
- Six Sigma
- Social Responsibility

Visit www.asq.org/training for more information.